Maneuvers with Fractions

Student Lab Book

David A. Page
Kathryn Chval

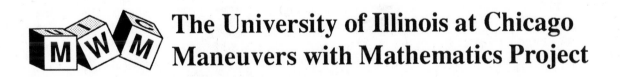

**The University of Illinois at Chicago
Maneuvers with Mathematics Project**

DALE SEYMOUR PUBLICATIONS

Other UIC-MWM Student Lab Books
Maneuvers with Rectangles
Maneuvers with Angles
Maneuvers with Triangles
Maneuvers with Nickels and Numbers
Maneuvers with Circles

(A Teacher Sourcebook is also available
for each Student Lab Book in the series.)

The Maneuvers with Mathematics Project materials were
prepared with the support of National Science Foundation
Grant Nos. MDR-8850466 and MDR-9154110. Any
opinions, findings, conclusions, or recommendations
expressed in this publication are those of the authors and
do not necessarily represent the views of the National
Science Foundation. These materials shall be subject to a
royalty-free, irrevocable, worldwide, nonexclusive
license for the United States Government to reproduce,
perform, translate, and otherwise use and to authorize
others to use such materials for Government purposes.

Order number DS21343
ISBN 0-86651-888-6

3 4 5 6 7 8 9 10-ML-98 97 96 95

This Book Is Printed
on Recycled Paper

Contents

1. Can You See What the Other Side Is Doing? 1

2. Finding Our Way with Proportions 19

3. It's a Matter of Time 33

4. On Top of the World 49

5. Bits and Pieces 57

6. How to Be Smarter Than Your Calculator 75

7. More or Less 91

8. The "Prime" Building Blocks 107

9. Traveling Through Time 119

10. One Good Operation Deserves Another 141

11. One in a Million 145

Essential contributions to UIC-MWM were made by:

John Baldwin
Roberta Dees
Steven Jordan

Janice Banasiak
Marty Gartzman
Olga Granat-Gonzalez
Michael Jankowski
Jennifer Lynná Mundt
Marlynne Nishimura
Pamela Piggeé
Jerome Pohlen
Mary Jo Porn
Mary Ann Schultz
Aimee W. Strawn

Production Assistants:

Lindy M. Chambers
Kimberly Hanus
Tanya Henderson
Tracy Ho
Alex Mak

Stacie McCloud
Monica Miller
Olga Vega
Wendy Wisneski

Graphic Artists:

Lisa Fucarino
Alex Mak

Illustrator:

Ben Nuñez

The University of Illinois at Chicago-Maneuvers with Mathematics (UIC-MWM) project started in July 1989 under the direction of David A. Page and Philip Wagreich of UIC. Earlier versions were tested in the following schools in Illinois:

Albright Middle School, Villa Park
Audubon Elementary School, Chicago
Benjamin Middle School, West Chicago
Caroline Bentley School, New Lenox
Daniel Boone Elementary School, Chicago
Carpenter School, Park Ridge
Central Jr. High School, Tinley Park
Christ the King School, Lombard
Nicholas Copernicus School, Chicago
Robert Emmet School, Chicago
Eugene Field Elementary School, Park Ridge
William G. Hibbard School, Chicago
Hillel Torah North Suburban Day School, Skokie
John L. Marsh Elementary School, Chicago
St. Germaine School, Oak Lawn
St. Joseph School, Chicago
St. Stephen Protomartyr School, Des Plaines
Mark Sheridan Math & Science Academy, Chicago
Washington Elementary School, Park Ridge
Wendell Smith Elementary School, Chicago

1. Can You See What the Other Side Is Doing?

Jasmine's allowance is $4. Her mother, Mrs. Vega, doubles Jasmine's allowance to $8. Jasmine's younger brother, Ben, has an allowance of $3. Mrs. Vega decides that it is only fair to double Ben's allowance to $6. The doubling of their allowances can be written as the following **proportion**.

$$4 : 8 :: 3 : 6$$

The proportion is read "4 is to 8 as 3 is to 6." This means that whatever you do to 4 to get 8, you also do the **same thing** to 3 to get 6.

4 : 8

3 : 6

1. The following proportion is read "5 is to 20 as 3 is to 12."

$$5 : 20 :: 3 : 12$$

What was done to 5 to get 20 and also to 3 to get 12? _____

2. The following proportion is read "18 is to 3 as 12 is to 2." Notice that a proportion has a **left-hand side** and a **right-hand side**.

$$18 : 3 :: 12 : 2$$

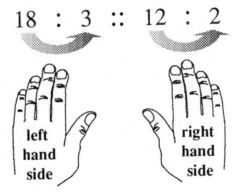

left hand side

right hand side

What was done to 18 on the left-hand side and also to 12 on the right-hand side?

Answer _____

Maneuvers with Fractions

The numbers in a proportion have names as shown below.

$$18 \ : \ 3 \ :: \ 12 \ : \ 2$$

first   second   third   fourth
term   term   term   term

3. The following are proportions. Write in what was done to the first and third terms to get the second and fourth terms on the answer lines. The first one is done for you.

a. 8 : 48 :: 5 : 30 ___×6___   b. 5 : 15 :: 6 : 18 _____

c. 25 : 5 :: 30 : 6 _____   d. 16 : 4 :: 12 : 3 _____

4. Last week, Jasmine received $8 and Ben received $6 for their allowances. They each spent half of their allowance on snacks. Fill in how much they spent on snacks in the following proportion.

Jasmine   Ben

$8 : $_____ :: $6 : $_____

5. Jasmine saved $30 and Ben saved $52. They each decided to contribute half of their savings for a family trip. Jasmine gave $15 from her savings. How much did Ben give? Fill in the fourth term in the following proportion.

$30 : $15 :: $52 : $_____

first   second   third   fourth
term   term   term   term

6. Fill in the fourth term in the following proportions.

a. 3 : 6 :: 5 : _____   b. 5 : 15 :: 50 : _____

c. 24 : 8 :: 30 : _____   d. 40 : 10 :: 76 : _____

e. 56 : 14 :: 84 : _____   f. 22 : 154 :: 17 : _____

Mr. Walt's class went to the local deli. The menu is shown below.

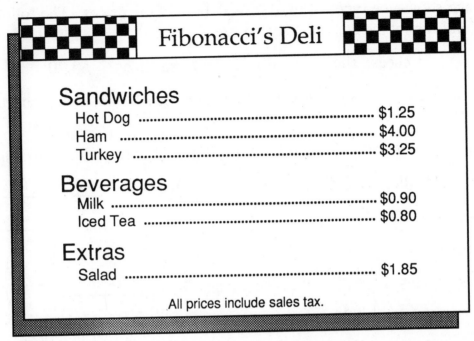

Fibonacci's Deli

Sandwiches
Hot Dog	$1.25
Ham	$4.00
Turkey	$3.25

Beverages
Milk	$0.90
Iced Tea	$0.80

Extras
Salad	$1.85

All prices include sales tax.

Tanji bought two ham sandwiches for a total of $8. Krista, Stephen, Elli, and Lena each bought a ham sandwich and their total bill was $16. Their math teacher, Mr. Walt, said, "It's proportional."

2 ham sandwiches ∶ $8 ∷ 4 ham sandwiches ∶ $16

7. Use the menu to complete the following proportions. Include the units. For example, "salads" and "$" are units.

7a. 1 hot dog ∶ $1.25 ∷ 5 hot dogs ∶ _____

7b. 5 turkey sandwiches ∶ _____ ∷ 2 turkey sandwiches ∶ $6.50

7c. 4 milks ∶ $3.60 ∷ _____ ∶ $5.40

7d. _____ ∶ 3 salads ∷ _____ ∶ 6 salads

7e. $4.80 ∶ _____ ∷ $8.00 ∶ _____

8. Make up a different proportion using the items from the menu above. Remember to include the units.

_____ ∶ _____ ∷ _____ ∶ _____

Mrs. Kinsella's class went to Pisa's Pizzas for lunch. The menu at the bottom of the page shows the types of food served, but not the prices. The following proportion is about the cost of cheese pizza slices.

1 cheese slice ∶ $1.60 ∷ 2 cheese slices ∶ $3.20

It is another way of saying, "If one cheese slice costs $1.60, then 2 cheese slices cost $3.20."

 9. Complete the following proportions. Remember to include missing units.

9a. 5 spinach slices ∶ $10.00 ∷ 1 spinach slice ∶ $_____

9b. 10 sausage slices ∶ $17.50 ∷ 1 sausage slice ∶ $_____

9c. 2 milks ∶ _____ ∷ 4 milks ∶ $2.40

9d. 2 lemonades ∶ $1.80 ∷ 10 lemonades ∶ _____

9e. 12 breadsticks ∶ $3.00 ∷ _____ ∶ $2.00

9f. _____ ∶ $11.70 ∷ 7 salads ∶ $13.65

10. Use the information in the proportions above to find the price of each item on the restaurant's menu. Write in the prices on the menu.

Pisa's Pizzas
Lunch Menu

Slices
Cheese ....$ _____
Sausage ....$ _____
Spinach ....$ _____

Beverages
Milk ....$ _____
Lemonade ....$ _____

Side Orders
Breadstick ....$ _____
Salad ....$ _____

---

11. Make up a different proportion using the items from the menu above. Remember to include the units.

_____ ∶ _____ ∷ _____ ∶ _____

12. On Monday, Bob bought 2 cheese slices at Pisa's Pizzas. On Tuesday, he doubled his order and bought 4 cheese slices. Bob's bill on Monday was $3.20. What was his bill on Tuesday? Write the amount in Bob's proportion.

2 cheese slices **:** $3.20 **::** 4 cheese slices **:** $_____

Bob's proportion could also be written the following ways.

$3.20 **:** 2 cheese slices **::** $6.40 **:** 4 cheese slices

or

4 cheese slices **:** $6.40 **::** 2 cheese slices **:** $3.20

13. Write a different proportion for Bob's two orders above. Remember to include units.

_____ **:** _____ **::** _____ **:** _____

14. Janson wrote the following:

2 cheese slices **:** $3.20 **::** $6.40 **:** 4 cheese slices

Janson's answer is **not** a proportion. What do you notice about the units in Janson's answer?

_____

15. Shirley wrote the following:

$3.20 **:** 2 cheese slices **::** 4 cheese slices **:** $6.40

Shirley's answer is **not** a proportion. What do you notice about the units in Shirley's answer?

_____

16. What can you say about the **units** on the left-hand side of a proportion as compared to the units on the right-hand side of that proportion?

_____

_____

Use the following pictures to answer the questions below.

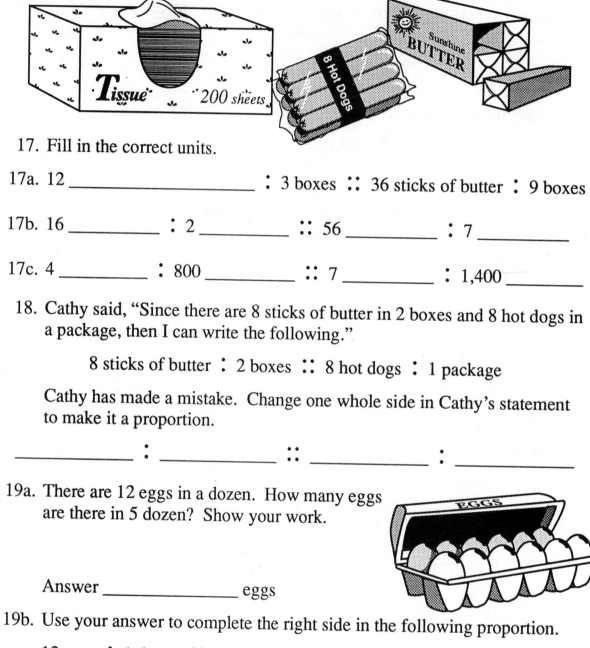

17. Fill in the correct units.

17a. 12 _____ : 3 boxes :: 36 sticks of butter : 9 boxes

17b. 16 _____ : 2 _____ :: 56 _____ : 7 _____

17c. 4 _____ : 800 _____ :: 7 _____ : 1,400 _____

18. Cathy said, "Since there are 8 sticks of butter in 2 boxes and 8 hot dogs in a package, then I can write the following."

    8 sticks of butter : 2 boxes :: 8 hot dogs : 1 package

Cathy has made a mistake. Change one whole side in Cathy's statement to make it a proportion.

_____ : _____ :: _____ : _____

19a. There are 12 eggs in a dozen. How many eggs are there in 5 dozen? Show your work.

    Answer _____ eggs

19b. Use your answer to complete the right side in the following proportion.

    12 eggs : 1 dozen :: _____ eggs : _____ dozen

20a. Mr. Eggert went to the grocery store to buy 300 eggs. How many dozen did Mr. Eggert buy? Show your work.

    Answer _____ dozen

20b. Use your answer to complete the following proportion.

    _____ eggs : _____ dozen :: _____ eggs : _____ dozen

21. The school dance committee wants to use the punch recipe at the right for its next event.

    This recipe will serve 15 students and the committee is expecting 150 students. Complete the following proportion to find how much ginger ale is needed.

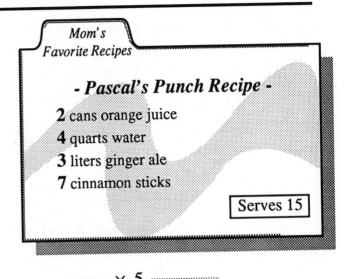

Mom's Favorite Recipes

- Pascal's Punch Recipe -

2 cans orange juice
4 quarts water
3 liters ginger ale
7 cinnamon sticks

Serves 15

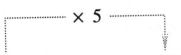

3 liters ginger ale **:** 15 students **::** _____ liters ginger ale **:** 150 students

22a. Keith said, "The recipe is written for 15 servings, but we want 150 servings. We need 10 times as many servings. $15 \times 10 = 150$, so we need to multiply each quantity in the recipe by 10." Keith set up the following proportion to find how many cinnamon sticks were needed. Complete Keith's proportion.

15 students **:** 150 students **::** 7 cinnamon sticks **:** _____ cinnamon sticks

22b. Look at the units in Keith's proportion above. Circle the unit "students" and underline the unit "cinnamon sticks."

22c. What do you notice about the units in this proportion? _____

    _____

23. Use Keith's method to find how many quarts of water are needed to serve 150 students.

    15 students **:** 150 students **::** _____ quarts **:** _____
    Put in units.

24. Washington School used the following Freshly Frozen Berry Yogurt recipe for their Annual Ice Cream Social.

Mom's Favorite Recipes

- Freshly Frozen Berry Yogurt -

16 pints strawberries

4 cups sugar

64 cups vanilla yogurt

Serves 88

24a. Taylor wanted to make 22 servings of this yogurt recipe for a family gathering. She wrote the following proportion to find how many pints of strawberries were needed.

88 servings **:** 22 servings **::** 16 pints **:** _____ pints

Taylor pressed the following keystrokes.

| 88 | ÷ | 22 | = |

The calculator window said, "4." So Taylor wrote:

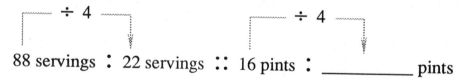

÷ 4   ÷ 4

88 servings **:** 22 servings **::** 16 pints **:** _____ pints

24b. Complete Taylor's recipe at the right. Show your work.

Mom's Favorite Recipes

- Taylor's Yogurt -

__4__ pints strawberries

___ cups sugar

___ cups vanilla yogurt

Serves 22

Another Relationship

Mrs. Keegan's seventh-grade class used the recipe at the right to make orange-glazed pecans for the Holiday Sale.

Bradley wrote a proportion to find how many cups of sugar are needed to make 24 servings. He did not see a "nice" relationship between the first and second terms, but he noticed another relationship in this proportion.

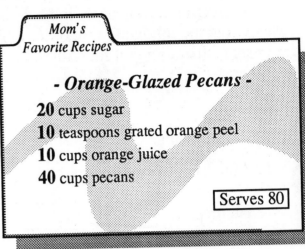

Mom's Favorite Recipes

- Orange-Glazed Pecans -

20 cups sugar
10 teaspoons grated orange peel
10 cups orange juice
40 cups pecans

Serves 80

÷ 4

80 servings : 24 servings :: 20 cups sugar : _____ cups sugar

÷ 4

1. How many cups of sugar are needed for 24 servings? _____

2a. On the following arrows, write the relationship between the first and third terms and between the second and fourth terms.

80 servings : 24 servings :: 10 cups juice : _____ cups juice

2b. Complete the proportion in Problem 2a.

3a. How many cups of pecans are needed for 80 servings? _____

3b. Set up a proportion to find how many cups of pecans are needed for 24 servings. Write the relationships on the arrows.

80 servings : _____ servings :: _____ cups pecans : _____ cups pecans

> In proportions, the relationship between the first and third terms is the same as the relationship between the second and fourth terms.

The Youth Center is making 1,360 servings of the orange-glazed pecan recipe. Alex and Priscilla wanted to find how many cups of sugar they will need. Alex wrote the following proportion. Notice that the letter *x* in the proportion represents the missing information, or the **unknown**.

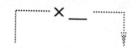

80 servings ∶ 1,360 servings ∷ 20 cups sugar ∶ *x* cups sugar

 4. Alex said, "What do I multiply 80 by to get 1,360?"

He pressed: | 1360 | ÷ | 80 | = |

4a. What did Alex see in the calculator window? Write your answer on the arrow above. This is the number Alex would multiply 80 by to get 1,360.

4b. What should Alex do to 20 to solve for the unknown? _____

4c. Alex used the keystrokes at the right for the entire problem. What is Alex's answer?

| 1360 | ÷ | 80 | = | × | 20 | = |

17 is in the window.

Answer _____ cups of sugar

5. Priscilla said, "What do I do to 80 to get 20?"

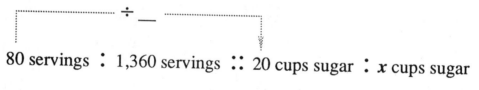

80 servings ∶ 1,360 servings ∷ 20 cups sugar ∶ *x* cups sugar

She pressed: | 80 | ÷ | 20 | = |

5a. What did Priscilla see in the calculator window? Write your answer on the arrow above. This is the number Priscilla would divide 80 by to get 20.

5b. What should Priscilla do to 1,360 to solve for the unknown? _____

5c. Priscilla used the keystrokes at the right for the entire problem. What is Priscilla's answer?

| 80 | ÷ | 20 | = | See 4 |
| 1360 | ÷ | 4 | = |

Answer _____ cups of sugar

Alex and Priscilla have good ways. Sometimes one way is easier than the other.

6. Answer the questions below using the following proportion.

$$5 : 35 :: 11 : a$$

6a. What should you multiply 5 by to get 35? _____

6b. What should you multiply 11 by? _____

6c. What is *a*? _____

7. Answer the questions below using the following proportion. Notice both arrows go in the same direction, but they point toward the left.

$$35 : b :: 5 : 11$$

7a. What should you multiply 5 by to get 35? _____

7b. What should you multiply 11 by? _____

7c. What is *b*? _____

8. Use arrows to write the relationship between the given terms. Then choose pairs of numbers from the answer column on the right to complete the proportions. Use each answer once. The first one is done for you.

Proportion	Answer Column

9 : ___5___ :: 81 : ___45___

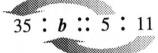

        11 and 55

3 : _____ :: 15 : _____

        65 and 13

_____ : 36 :: _____ : 4

        5 and 45

19 : _____ :: 95 : _____

        72 and 8

_____ : 60 :: _____ : 12

        6 and 30

9. Solve the following proportions without a calculator. Use arrows to show the relationships. The first one is done for you.

c : 2 :: 21 : 7 $c =$ _____ 6 _____

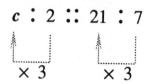

3 : 8 :: 15 : d $d =$ _____

18 : 3 :: 30 : e $e =$ _____

6 : 54 :: 5 : f $f =$ _____

g : 10 :: 24 : 8 $g =$ _____

 10. Use your calculator to solve the following proportions. Write your keystrokes in the blank boxes. You do not have to use all the boxes.

469 : 938 :: 1 : h $h =$ _____

938 : 1 :: 469 : j $j =$ _____

The answer is not 2.

11 : 4 :: k : 96 $k =$ _____

m : 595 :: 56 : 476 $m =$ _____

Going to Extremes

The inside terms in a proportion are called the **means** and the outside terms are called the **extremes**.

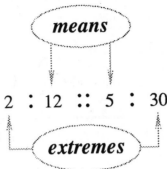

1. Find the **product** of the means.
   (To find the product, multiply.)

   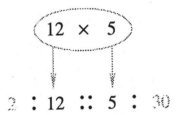

   Product of the means _____

2. Find the product of the extremes.

   Product of the extremes _____

3. Complete the following table. The first one is done for you.

Proportion	Means	Product of the Means	Extremes	Product of the Extremes
2 : 12 :: 5 : 30	12 and 5	12 × 5 = 60	2 and 30	2 × 30 = 60
5 : 7 :: 50 : 70	and		and	
89 : 356 :: 13 : 52	and		and	
900 : 150 :: 90 : 15	and		and	

4. What do you notice about the **product of the means** compared to the **product of the extremes** in each proportion in the table?

_____

5. In a proportion, the product of the means equals the product of the extremes.

$$50 : 3 :: 9 : 150$$

5a. What is the product of the means? _____

5b. What is the product of the extremes? _____

5c. Is $50 : 3 :: 9 : 150$ a proportion? _____
                                              Yes or No

> The following proportion compares inches and feet.
>
> $$24 \text{ inches} : 2 \text{ feet} :: 48 \text{ inches} : 4 \text{ feet}$$
>
> The product of the means is $2 \text{ feet} \times 48 \text{ inches} = 96 \text{ feet inches}$.
>
> The product of the extremes is $24 \text{ inches} \times 4 \text{ feet} = 96 \text{ inches feet}$.
>
> **"Feet inches" is the same unit as "inches feet."**
>
> Notice that **both** the products of the **numbers** and the **units** are the same. "Feet inches" may look like a strange notation, but it is a good way to make sure the proportion is set up correctly.

6. We rearranged the proportion.

$$24 \text{ inches} : 48 \text{ inches} :: 2 \text{ feet} : 4 \text{ feet}$$

6a. What is the product of the means? _____
                                              Put in strange units.

6b. What is the product of the extremes? _____
                                              Put in strange units.

6c. Are the products equal? _____
                          Yes or No

7. Carefully look at the units in the following problems. Write "Y" if they are proportions and write "N" if they are not.

$$\underline{\qquad} \quad 24 \text{ inches} : 2 \text{ feet} \overset{?}{::} 36 \text{ inches} : 3 \text{ feet}$$

$$\underline{\qquad} \quad 12 \text{ inches} : 1 \text{ foot} \overset{?}{::} 3 \text{ feet} : 36 \text{ inches}$$

$$\underline{\qquad} \quad 24 \text{ inches} : 6 \text{ feet} \overset{?}{::} 7 \text{ feet} : 28 \text{ inches}$$

$$\underline{\qquad} \quad 8 \text{ feet} : 5 \text{ feet} \overset{?}{::} 96 \text{ inches} : 60 \text{ inches}$$

Tiny Measurements

1. How could you measure the thickness of this sheet of paper using a ruler?

   Answer _____

2. Veronica decided to measure a stack of paper in order to find the thickness of one sheet. Paper comes in packages called "reams."
   Each ream of paper contains 500 sheets. Veronica measured the thickness of a ream of paper. She measured 5.0 cm. Then she set up the following proportion.

   500 sheets ∶ 5.0 cm ∷ 1 sheet ∶ x cm

   How thick is one sheet of her paper?

   Thickness _____ cm

3. What is the thickness of a one-dollar bill? Is it the same as a sheet of Veronica's paper? Since a one-dollar bill is thin, it is too difficult to measure directly with your ruler. According to the United States government, the height of a stack of 100 new one-dollar bills is 1.0922 cm.

3a. Set up a proportion to find the thickness of one bill. Include a letter for the unknown.

   100 bills ∶ 1.0922 cm ∷ _____ bill ∶ _____ cm

3b. Solve the proportion. Notice two of the digits are given.

   Thickness of one bill ☐.☐☐ 0 9 ☐☐ cm

3c. Round your answer to the nearest thousandth of a cm.

   Thickness of one bill _____ cm

4. Which is thicker, a dollar bill or one piece of Veronica's paper?

   Answer _____

Bill or Paper

5a. Look at a penny. Is the thickness of a penny more or less than 1 cm?

Answer _____
More or Less

5b. Is the thickness of a penny more or less than 0.1 cm? _____
More or Less

5c. What is the thickness of a penny? Stack some pennies, as shown at the right, and measure the height of your stack to the nearest 0.1 cm. (You may use any number of pennies.)

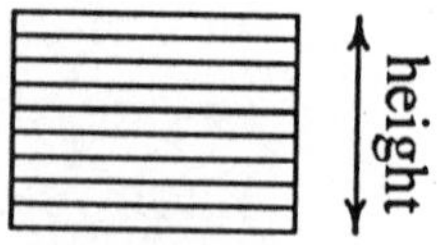

9 pennies ↕ height

Number of pennies stacked _____

Height of stack _____ cm

6a. Use your data from Problem 5c to find the average thickness of one penny.

_____ pennies **:** _____ cm **::** 1 penny **:** x cm

6b. Solve for the unknown. Thickness of one penny _____ cm
R to the nearest tenth.

7. Estimate how many "e's" could be typed in the following box.

eeee

Estimate _____

8. Now count how many "e's" fit in the box.

eeeeeeeeeeeeeeeeeeeeeeeeeeeeeeeeeeeeeeeeeeeeeeeeeeeeeeeeeeeeeeeeeeeeeeeee

Answer _____

9a. How could you find the width of the letter "e" in the figures above?

_____

_____

9b. Use a proportion to find the width of the letter "e" to the nearest 0.01 cm. Show your work.

Width of "e" _____ cm
R to the nearest hundredth.

Homework 1: Can You See What the Other Side Is Doing?

The students in Mr. Laeti's art class used the recipe at the right to make clay.

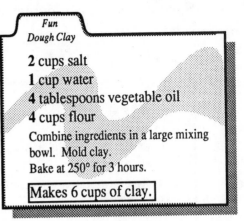

Fun
Dough Clay

2 cups salt
1 cup water
4 tablespoons vegetable oil
4 cups flour
Combine ingredients in a large mixing bowl. Mold clay.
Bake at 250° for 3 hours.

Makes 6 cups of clay.

1. If each of the 32 students in the class brought in 1 cup of flour, how many cups of clay could they make? (Assume there is enough salt, water, and vegetable oil to go with the flour.) Set up and solve a proportion.

    Answer _____ cups of clay

2a. How many tablespoons of vegetable oil would be required for a recipe with 32 cups of flour?

    Answer _____ tablespoons

2b. There are 16 tablespoons in a cup. How many cups of vegetable oil would Mr. Laeti's class need? Set up a proportion and solve.

    Answer _____ cups of vegetable oil

3. Bryant wants to make some clay at home. He only has 3 cups of flour, but the recipe calls for 4 cups. If he uses 3 cups of flour, he will need less salt, water, and vegetable oil. Fill out the new recipe card for Bryant.

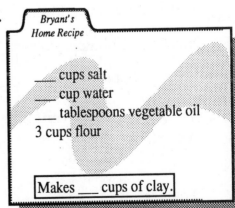

Bryant's
Home Recipe

___ cups salt
___ cup water
___ tablespoons vegetable oil
3 cups flour

Makes ___ cups of clay.

4. All of the students at Mr. Laeti's school decided to make animal figures to sell at the Student Fair. Two cups of clay will make nine animals. Each of the 450 students will make 3 animals to sell. Complete the whole school's recipe.

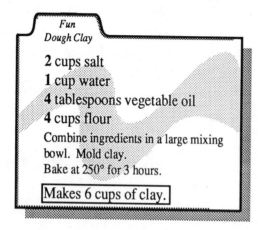

Fun Dough Clay

2 cups salt
1 cup water
4 tablespoons vegetable oil
4 cups flour

Combine ingredients in a large mixing bowl. Mold clay.
Bake at 250° for 3 hours.

Makes 6 cups of clay.

The School's Recipe

___ cups salt
___ cups water
___ tablespoons vegetable oil
___ cups flour

Makes ___ cups of clay.

5. Ryan collects baseball trading cards. He stacked 113 cards and measured the height of his stack. If the height of Ryan's stack was 4.5 cm, what would be the height of 67 cards? Show your proportion.

Answer _____ cm
R to the nearest tenth.

6a. Find several identical flat objects. For example, you can use a deck of playing cards, trading cards, records, crackers, etc.

Type of object _____

6b. Stack many copies of your object.
Measure the stack to the nearest 0.1 cm.

Number of objects stacked _____

Height of stack _____
Put in units.

6c. If 1,000 copies of your object were stacked, what would be the height of your stack? Show your proportion.

Answer _____
Put in units.

6d. What is the thickness of one of your objects?

Answer _____ cm
R to the nearest tenth.

2. Finding Our Way with Proportions

The only true maps of the world are on **globes**. Measuring distances on a globe can be tricky. If a curved piece of a globe is flattened out, it is no longer completely accurate because it is stretched. Small parts of the globe, like the United States, flatten out quite well. The following is an example of a **flat map**. You can measure distances on this flat map and still be quite accurate.

Here is a map of the Continental United States (without Alaska and Hawaii).

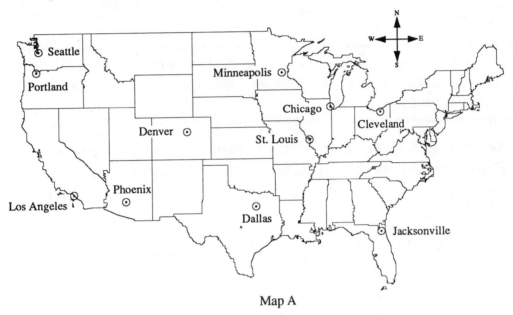

Map A

 1. The actual airline distance between Denver, Colorado and Minneapolis, Minnesota, is 700 miles. Draw a line between Denver and Minneapolis. Measure the distance to the nearest 0.1 cm on the map above.

Measured distance _____ cm

2a. Do you think the actual distance between Dallas, Texas and Chicago, Illinois, is more than 700 miles or less than 700 miles?

Answer _____
More or Less

2b. What is your quick "eyeball" estimate? _____ miles

 3. Draw a line between Dallas and Chicago. Measure the distance to the nearest 0.1 cm.

Measured distance _____ cm

4a. In this problem, the actual distance between Denver and Minneapolis is given as 700 miles. Complete the missing information on the proportion below.

Denver to Minneapolis (Measured)	:	Denver to Minneapolis (Actual)	::	Dallas to Chicago (Measured)	:	Dallas to Chicago (Actual)
_____ cm	:	700 miles	::	_____ cm	:	*x* miles

4b. Now solve for the actual distance between Dallas and Chicago.

x = _____ miles

<small>R to the nearest mile.</small>

Proportions are used to find the actual distances between places. The distances vary depending on the accuracy of the map and the measurements.

---

5. When Map A (page 19) was drawn, the measured distance between Denver and Minneapolis was set at 3.0 cm. Complete and solve the following proportion to find out how many miles 1 cm represents on Map A.

1 cm : *x* miles :: _____ cm : _____ miles

1 cm : _____ miles

<small>R to the nearest mile.</small>

The left side of this proportion is a *scale* for Map A. A scale compares measured and actual distances.

measured : actual

or

actual : measured

6. Three students measured the distance between Dallas and Chicago. Calculate each student's actual distance using the scale for Map A.

Student	Measured Distance	Proportion	Actual Distance
Zachary	3.4 cm		miles
Darea	3.3 cm		miles
Greg	3.2 cm		miles

7. Darea's and Zachary's measurements only differed by 0.1 cm.
   However, their actual distances differ by many miles.
   Complete and solve the following proportion to find how many miles are
   represented by 0.1 cm.

   1 cm $:$ _____ miles $::$ 0.1 cm $:$ x miles

   x = _____ miles

8. What is the difference between Zachary's and Darea's actual distances?

   Answer _____ miles

9. Why did Zachary, Darea, and Greg get different answers for x?

   _____

10a. What is the range of their **measured** distances?

   _____

10b. What is the range of their **actual** distances?

   _____

11a. Measure the distance between Chicago and Minneapolis to the nearest
    0.1 cm using Map A on page 19.

    Measured distance _____ cm

11b. Calculate the actual distance between these two cities.
    Write your proportion and solve for x. Remember to include the units.

    _____ $:$ _____ $::$ _____ $:$ _____

    Actual distance _____ miles
    <small>R to the nearest mile.</small>

Maps come in many different sizes. The following map shows seven states from the North Central United States.

12a. Measure the distance between Chicago and Minneapolis to the nearest 0.1 cm.

Measured distance _____ cm

12b. Why is this measurement different from Problem 11a?

_____

_____

_____

12c. Does the actual distance between Chicago and Minneapolis change?

Answer _____
        Yes or No

12d. What is the actual distance? _____
                          Answer to Problem 11b

Minneapolis ☉

Lake Michigan

Chicago ☉

St. Louis ☉

Scale

1 cm ⦂ _____ miles

Map B

13a. Complete and solve the following proportion to determine a scale for Map B. Remember to include units.

_____ ⦂ _____ ⦂⦂ 1 cm ⦂ x miles

1 cm ⦂ _____ miles
       R to the nearest mile.

13b. Write the scale on Map B.

14a. Measure the distance between Chicago and St. Louis on Map B to the nearest 0.1 cm.

Measured distance _____ cm

14b. Write a proportion and calculate the actual distance between these two cities.

Actual distance _____ miles
                R to the nearest mile.

15. Label the names of the seven states on Map B above.

16. The countries of Great Britain and
France are separated by a narrow
strip of water called the Strait
of Dover. The Strait stretches
21 miles between Calais,
France, and Dover, Great Britain.
Use Map C to determine a scale.
Write the scale on Map C.

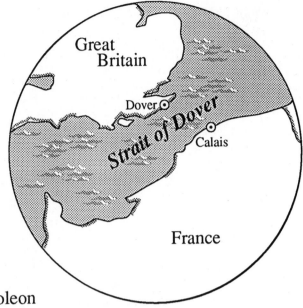

Travel between Great Britain and
France has always been by boat,
plane, or hovercraft. For hundreds
of years, people have dreamed of
building a tunnel under the Strait.
The first plan was approved by Napoleon
in 1802, but the project failed, as did many
others. In 1990, engineers completed the
first Channel Tunnel, or Chunnel, which
connects Dover and Calais. The first train is
scheduled to pass through the Chunnel in
early 1994.

```
+-----------------------------+
|            Scale            |
| 1 cm  :  _____ miles      |
+-----------------------------+
```
Map C

17. The Chunnel is 33 miles long. How many centimeters is that on Map C?

Answer _____ cm

18. Why is the Chunnel longer than the distance between Dover and Calais?

_____

_____

19. The total cost of the Chunnel was $14 billion dollars. Complete the
following proportion to determine the cost of one average mile in billions
of dollars.

_____ miles : $_____ billion :: 1 mile : $$x$ billion

x = $_____ billion
    R to the nearest hundredth.

20. What would one mile cost, in **millions** of dollars?

Answer $_____ million

Try It Out!

The following map shows several interesting places you might want to visit.

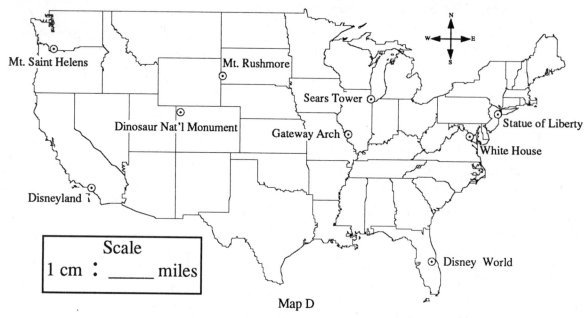

Map D

  1a. The actual distance between Dinosaur National Monument and Mt. Saint Helens is 775 miles. Measure this distance to the nearest 0.1 cm.

Measured distance _____ cm

1b. Calculate the scale for Map D. Round to the nearest whole mile. Write the scale on Map D.

2. Place a dot on Map D that shows where you live.

  3. Measure the distance between your city and Disney World to the nearest 0.1 cm.

Measured distance _____
                            Put in units.

4a. Write a proportion to find the actual distance between your city and Disney World.

_____ : _____ :: _____ : _____

  4b. Find the actual distance between your city and Disney World.

Actual distance _____ miles
                        R to the nearest mile.

5a. Adrian was flying from Chicago (Sears Tower) to Disney World, but her flight had to stop in Washington D.C. (White House) or St. Louis (Gateway Arch) on the way. Draw the two different routes on Map D.

5b. Without solving for the actual distances, which route is shorter?

Through _____

<small>Washington D.C. or St. Louis</small>

6. Adrian's plane flew the shorter route. How many miles did Adrian's plane fly? Show your work.

Actual distance _____ miles

<small>R to the nearest mile.</small>

7. What is the difference between the longer route and the shorter route? Show your work.

Answer _____ miles

8a. Place and label a dot on Map D to indicate the location of a place you want to visit.

Name of place _____

8b. Calculate the actual distance to this location. Show your work.

Actual distance _____ miles

<small>R to the nearest mile.</small>

9a. You have just won a contest sponsored by Express Airlines. They will award you 3,000 free air miles within the Continental United States. Where do you want to go? You must start and end at your hometown. Travel to as many places on Map D as you can, but remember you cannot travel more than 3,000 miles. Plot your course on Map D.

9b. What is the most, in centimeters, you can travel on the map?

Answer _____ cm

9c. How many centimeters **did** you travel on the map? _____ cm

9d. How many miles did you fly? _____ miles

9e. List the places you visited. _____

10. The following map shows eleven corporate headquarters. Two of the headquarters are labeled. On this map, 1.1 cm represents 256 miles. You are given the **actual** distances between the corporate headquarters below. Solve for the **measured** distances. Then decide which dot represents that headquarters. Write the name of the corporations on the map as you go along. The first problem has been started for you.

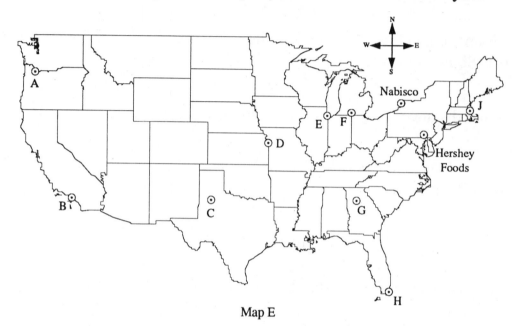

Map E

10a. The distance between Nabisco and Texas Instruments is 1,350 miles.

$$1.1 \text{ cm} : 256 \text{ miles} :: x \text{ cm} : 1,350 \text{ miles}$$

What is the measured distance? _____5.8_____ cm

R to the nearest tenth.

Remember to write "Texas Instruments" beside the dot 5.8 cm away from Nabisco.

10b. The distance between Texas Instruments and Sega is 514 miles.

What is the measured distance? _____ cm

R to the nearest tenth.

10c. The distance between Sega and Nike is 1,550 miles.

What is the measured distance? _____ cm

R to the nearest tenth.

10d. The distance between Nike and Coca-Cola is 2,207 miles.

What is the measured distance? _____ cm

R to the nearest tenth.

10e. The distance between Coca-Cola and Mattel is 1,827 miles.

What is the measured distance? _____ cm

R to the nearest tenth.

10f. The distance between Mattel and Parker Brothers is 2,605 miles.

What is the measured distance? _____ cm

R to the nearest tenth.

10g. The distance between Parker Brothers and Quaker Oats is 911 miles.

What is the measured distance? _____ cm

R to the nearest tenth.

10h. The distance between Quaker Oats and Burger King is 1,150 miles.

What is the measured distance? _____ cm

R to the nearest tenth.

10j. The distance between Burger King and Kellogg is 1,133 miles.

What is the measured distance? _____ cm

R to the nearest tenth.

11. Ten cities are listed below. Use Map E on page 26 to match the corporate headquarters with these cities.

11a. Hershey, Pennsylvania _____

11b. Miami, Florida _____

11c. Chicago, Illinois _____

11d. Beaverton, Oregon _____

11e. Niagara Falls, New York _____

11f. Shawnee Mission, Kansas _____

11g. Beverly, Massachusetts _____

11h. Hawthorne, California _____

11j. Battle Creek, Michigan _____

11k. Lubbock, Texas _____

12a. Which corporate headquarters was not matched with a city? _____

12b. In which state is that corporation located? _____

Homework 2: Finding Our Way with Proportions

Use the following map of Fraction Island to answer the questions below.

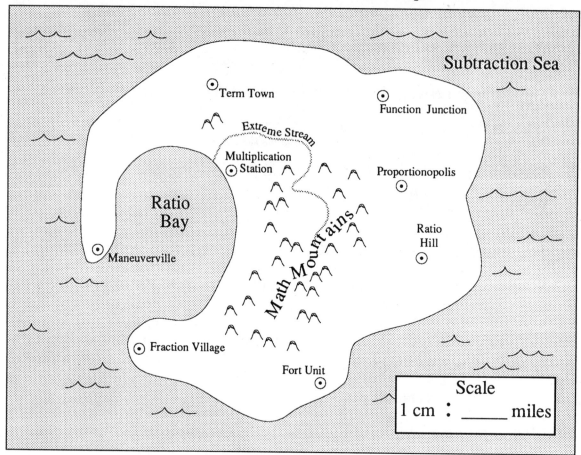

Map F

 1a. The actual distance between Maneuverville and Function Junction is 308 miles. Measure this distance to the nearest 0.1 cm.

Measured distance _____ cm

 1b. Find the scale for Map F using the following proportion.

_____ cm ⦂ 308 miles ⦂⦂ 1 cm ⦂ x miles
   Answer to Problem 1a

1c. Write the scale on Map F above. Round to the nearest mile.

2. Use the scale for Map F to determine the actual distance between Fraction Village and Proportionopolis.

Actual distance _____ miles
   R to the nearest mile.

3. The citizens of Maneuverville and Fraction Village are looking for a way to travel between their two cities. They can build a railroad around the shores of Ratio Bay or construct an extension bridge across it.
The railroad would cost a total of $835 million. A bridge would cost $9 million for each mile. Use the following steps to find the less expensive way to connect the cities.

3a. What is the actual distance between Maneuverville and Fraction Village?

Actual distance _____ miles
R to the nearest tenth.

3b. How much would the bridge cost? Complete the proportion and solve. Remember to include the units.

$9 million : 1 mile :: _____ : _____

Cost $_____ million
R to the nearest million.

3c. Which is the cheaper way to connect the cities? _____
Railroad or Bridge

4. City planners came up with another idea. They proposed to dig a tunnel under Ratio Bay. It would cost $6 million for each mile to dig the hole and another $270 million to pave a road through the tunnel.
Use the following steps to decide if they should build the tunnel.

4a. How much would it cost to dig the tunnel? Complete the proportion and solve. Remember to include the units.

$6 million : 1 mile :: _____ : _____

Cost to dig the tunnel $_____ million
R to the nearest million.

4b. What would be the entire cost of the tunnel project?

Cost $_____ million
R to the nearest million.

5. Which is the least expensive proposal to connect Maneuverville and Fraction Village?

Answer _____

Use the enlarged map of a part of Fraction Island to answer the questions below.

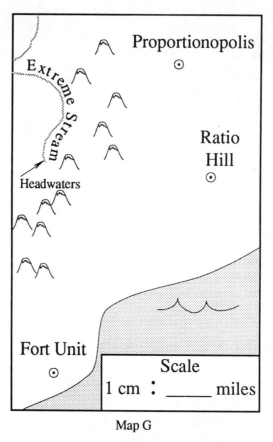

Map G

 6a. The actual distance between Fort Unit and Proportionopolis is 200 miles. What is the measured distance between these two cities?

Measured distance _____ cm

 6b. Complete and solve the following proportion to find the scale for Map G.

200 miles : _____ cm :: x miles : 1 cm

6c. Write the scale on the map above. Round to the nearest tenth.

Legend has it that a treasure is buried in the Math Mountains. A local librarian uncovered instructions, at the right, on finding its location.

Solve the problem on your own or use the steps on the next page.

Leave Proportionopolis heading directly toward Fort Unit. Go 98 miles. Turn and head directly toward the headwaters (beginning) of Extreme Stream. Go 21 miles. Turn and head toward Fort Unit. Go 56 miles. Stop, and dig under the big oak tree by the boulder.

Use the steps in Problems 7 through 9 to find the buried treasure.

7a. Draw a straight line between Fort Unit and Proportionopolis.

7b. Use a proportion to find how many centimeters represent 98 miles. The left side of the proportion is the scale for Map G (page 30).

_____ miles ⋮ 1 cm ∷ 98 miles ⋮ x cm

Answer _____ cm
<small>R to the nearest tenth.</small>

7c. To find the treasure, start at Proportionopolis and walk 98 miles toward Fort Unit. Place a "⊙" on your line that is 98 miles from Proportionopolis.

8a. Draw a straight line between the ⊙ and the headwaters of Extreme Stream.

8b. Use a proportion to find how many centimeters represent 21 miles. The left side of the proportion is the scale for Map G.

_____ miles ⋮ 1 cm ∷ 21 miles ⋮ x cm

Answer _____ cm
<small>R to the nearest tenth.</small>

8c. To find the treasure, start at ⊙ and walk 21 miles toward the headwaters. Place a "△" 21 miles from ⊙.

9a. Draw a straight line between the △ and Fort Unit.

9b. Use a proportion to find how many centimeters represent 56 miles. The left side of the proportion is the scale for Map G.

_____ miles ⋮ 1 cm ∷ 56 miles ⋮ x cm

Answer _____ cm
<small>R to the nearest tenth.</small>

9c. To find the treasure, start at △ and walk 56 miles toward Fort Unit. Place an "**X**" 56 miles from △. The **X** marks the spot for the buried treasure. On the map, the treasure should be 4.7 cm, 4.8 cm, or 4.9 cm from Ratio Hill. How close is your **X** to Ratio Hill?

Answer _____ cm

10. What treasure is buried in the Math Mountains? _____

Use the following map to answer the questions below.

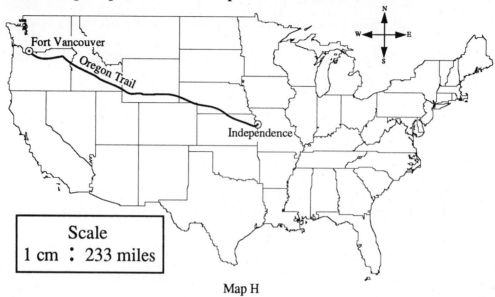

Map H

 11. The Oregon Trail stretched 2,000 miles from Independence, Missouri, to
Fort Vancouver, Washington. Draw a straight line from Independence to
Fort Vancouver. How far would a plane travel flying directly from
Independence to Fort Vancouver? Show your work.

Answer _____ miles

R to the nearest mile.

12a. How many more miles did the pioneers in 1860 have to travel from
Independence to reach Fort Vancouver than a plane does today?

Answer _____ miles

R to the nearest mile.

12b. Why did the pioneers travel so much farther? _____

_____

3. It's a Matter of Time

Have you ever thought about how you spend your time? How long you spend eating meals? How long you are in school? How long you spend sleeping?

Miss Nishimura wanted her classes to investigate how they spent one of their days. She gave each student the following table to complete. One student, Drenda, completed the middle column as follows.

Activity	Amount of Time Spent	Amount of Time Spent in Minutes
Sleeping	8 hours	
Getting Ready for School	45 minutes	45 minutes
Eating Breakfast	20 minutes	20 minutes
Brushing Teeth	45 seconds	
Eating Lunch	25 minutes	25 minutes
Attending Classes	5.25 hours	
Getting to and from school	20 minutes	20 minutes
Doing Homework	1 hour	
Eating Dinner	40 minutes	40 minutes
Watching TV	2 hours	
Basketball Practice	1 hour	
Reading	1 hour	
Talking on Phone	35 minutes	35 minutes

1. Notice that Drenda used different time units in her table. In order to compare the amount of time spent on different activities, it is practical to use the same unit. Solve the following proportion to find how many **minutes** Drenda spends sleeping.

$$60 \text{ minutes} : 1 \text{ hour} :: x \text{ minutes} : 8 \text{ hours}$$

Write your answer in the table above. Include the units.

2. Complete the table by changing all of Drenda's units to minutes.

3. There are 24 hours in a day. Use the following proportion to calculate how many minutes are in one day.

$$60 \text{ minutes} : 1 \text{ hour} :: m \text{ minutes} : 24 \text{ hours}$$

Answer _____ minutes in a day

4. How many total minutes did Drenda record in her table? _____

Put in units.

5. How many minutes does she have left in her day? _____

Put in units.

6. How do you spend your time? Keep track of how you spend the next 24 hours using the following table.

Activity	Amount of Time Spent *Put in units.*	Amount of Time Spent in Minutes
Sleeping		
Getting Ready for School		
Eating Breakfast		
Brushing Teeth		
Eating Lunch		
Attending Classes		

7. Using proportions, change all the time units to minutes in the table above. Show your work on a separate piece of paper.

8. How many total minutes did you record in your table? _____

9. How many minutes are left over? _____

Beside or Below, It's a Proportion

Edgar, a student in Miss Nishimura's class, spends 7.5 hours of his day sleeping. The following proportion shows how many minutes he sleeps.

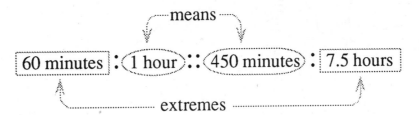

1. What is the product of the means? _____
   Put in strange units.

2. What is the product of the extremes? _____
   Put in strange units.

Edgar's proportion can also be written as two equal **fractions**.

$$\left(60 \text{ minutes} : 1 \text{ hour}\right) :: \left(450 \text{ minutes} : 7.5 \text{ hours}\right)$$

$$\frac{60 \text{ minutes}}{1 \text{ hour}} = \frac{450 \text{ minutes}}{7.5 \text{ hours}}$$

The left side, $\frac{60 \text{ minutes}}{1 \text{ hour}}$, is a **fraction** and can be read, "60 minutes **per** 1 hour."

The right side, $\frac{450 \text{ minutes}}{7.5 \text{ hours}}$, is a **fraction** and can be read, "450 minutes **per** 7.5 hours."

In the following figure, the extremes are in boxes and the means are in loops.

$$\frac{60 \text{ minutes}}{1 \text{ hour}} = \frac{450 \text{ minutes}}{7.5 \text{ hours}}$$

The following arrows show diagonals. Multiply along each arrow to get the product of the means and extremes including the units. If the product of the means equals the product of the extremes, then the statement is a proportion. When you multiply along the diagonals, it is often called *cross multiplication*.

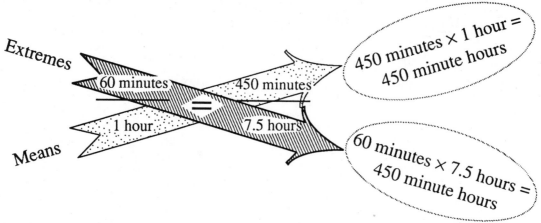

3. Cecilia spent 1.5 hours on homework. She then wrote the following.

$$\frac{60 \text{ minutes}}{1 \text{ hour}} = \frac{90 \text{ minutes}}{1.5 \text{ hours}}$$

3a. Draw a diagonal line through the extremes. **Cross multiply.**

60 minutes × 1.5 hours = _____

Put in strange units.

3b. Draw a diagonal line through the means. **Cross multiply.**

1 hour × 90 minutes = _____

Put in strange units.

You can write your strange units as "**minute hours**" or "**hour minutes.**" Both ways are the same.

4. Use cross multiplication to decide whether the following is a proportion. Write each diagonal product and its **units** in the bubbles.

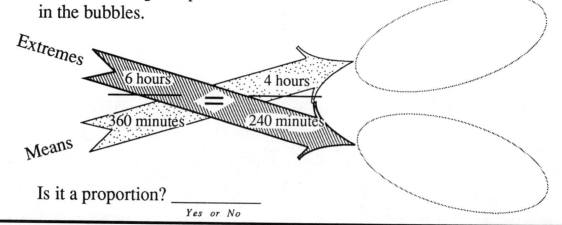

Is it a proportion? _____

Yes or No

5. Use cross multiplication to decide whether the following are proportions. Calculate each diagonal product including units. Then write "yes" or "no" to tell if it is a proportion.

	Proportion?	One Diagonal Product	Other Diagonal Product	Yes or No
a.	$\dfrac{5 \text{ hours}}{300 \text{ minutes}} \overset{?}{=} \dfrac{7 \text{ hours}}{420 \text{ minutes}}$			
b.	$\dfrac{3 \text{ hours}}{180 \text{ minutes}} \overset{?}{=} \dfrac{240 \text{ minutes}}{4 \text{ hours}}$			
c.	$\dfrac{120 \text{ seconds}}{2 \text{ hours}} \overset{?}{=} \dfrac{180 \text{ minutes}}{3 \text{ hours}}$			
d.	$\dfrac{30 \text{ seconds}}{60 \text{ seconds}} \overset{?}{=} \dfrac{2 \text{ minutes}}{4 \text{ minutes}}$			

You can use your calculator's memory to check the diagonal products of a proportion; however, **the calculator will not check the products of the units for you.** The following figure shows some of the keys for the TI-30 SLR+™. The **memory** keys are shaded.

STO means **Store**. It takes a copy of the number in the window and puts it into the memory.

RCL means **Recall**. It takes a copy of the number in memory and puts it in the window.

SUM means **Sum**. It adds the number in the window to the number in the memory.

EXC means **Exchange**. It swaps the number in the memory and the number in the window.

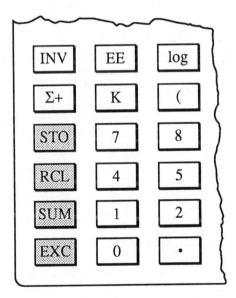

Beware! Do not use AC/ON when you use the memory. If you want to clear the window and **keep** the number in the memory, press CE/C **twice**.

6. See if the following statement is a proportion using the steps below.

$$\frac{4 \text{ years}}{1{,}464 \text{ days}} \overset{?}{=} \frac{8 \text{ years}}{2{,}922 \text{ days}}$$

6a. **First** check the units. Are the products of the units equal? _____

Yes or No

6b. If the answer is "No," the statement is not a proportion. Use the following keystrokes to multiply two numbers on one diagonal and [STO]re the answer in memory.

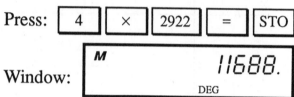

Press: | 4 | × | 2922 | = | STO |

Window:

M   *11688.*

                    DEG

Notice the **M** in the window. The **M** means you have a number in **M**emory.

6c. When you pressed [STO], you put 11,688 into memory. 11,688 will stay in memory until you change it with a memory key or press [AC/ON].

Now find the other diagonal product using the following keystrokes.

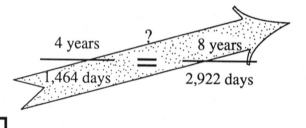

Press: | 1464 | × | 8 | = |

Window:

M   *11712.*

                    DEG

One diagonal product is in the window and the other diagonal product is in the memory. But are they the same?

Press: [EXC]   ⟵   This exchanges or swaps the window and the memory.

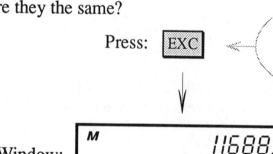

Window:

M   *11688.*

                    DEG

If the numbers change in the window, the diagonal products are **not** equal and the statement is **not** a proportion. If nothing changes when you press [EXC], then the number in the memory is the same as the number in the window. The diagonal products are equal.

6d. Did the numbers change in Problem 6c? _____
                                                    Yes or No

6e. Is $\dfrac{4 \text{ years}}{1{,}464 \text{ days}} \overset{?}{=} \dfrac{8 \text{ years}}{2{,}922 \text{ days}}$ a proportion? _____
                                                    Yes or No

---

If the calculator tells you the diagonal products are equal and you know the products of the units are equal, then the statement is a proportion.

---

7. Use the calculator's memory and the steps below to see if the following is a proportion.

$$\frac{15 \text{ years}}{5{,}478.75 \text{ days}} \overset{?}{=} \frac{12 \text{ years}}{4{,}386 \text{ days}}$$

7a. Are the products of the **units** the same? _____
                                                    Yes or No

7b. Press: [15] [×] [4386] [=] [STO]

7c. Press: [5478.75] [×] [12] [=] [EXC]

7d. Did the numbers change? _____
                                    Yes or No

7e. Is $\dfrac{15 \text{ years}}{5{,}478.75 \text{ days}} \overset{?}{=} \dfrac{12 \text{ years}}{4{,}386 \text{ days}}$ a proportion? _____
                                                    Yes or No

8. Use [STO], [EXC], and cross multiplication to decide whether the following are proportions. Remember to check the products of the units first. Write "yes" or "no" on the answer line.

$$\frac{3{,}600 \text{ seconds}}{1{,}800 \text{ seconds}} \overset{?}{=} \frac{1 \text{ hour}}{0.5 \text{ hours}}$$

8a. Are the products of the units the same? _____
                                                    Yes or No

8b. List your keystrokes to check the diagonal products.

You do not have to use all the keystroke boxes.

8c. Is it a proportion? _____
                            Yes or No

8d. $\dfrac{780 \text{ minutes}}{13 \text{ hours}} \overset{?}{=} \dfrac{780 \text{ seconds}}{13 \text{ minutes}}$ _____
Yes or No

8e. $\dfrac{10{,}080 \text{ minutes}}{1 \text{ week}} \overset{?}{=} \dfrac{2 \text{ weeks}}{20{,}160 \text{ minutes}}$ _____
Yes or No

8 f. $\dfrac{52 \text{ weeks}}{1 \text{ year}} \overset{?}{=} \dfrac{156 \text{ weeks}}{3 \text{ years}}$ _____
Yes or No

8g. $\dfrac{10 \text{ weeks}}{18 \text{ hours}} \overset{?}{=} \dfrac{85 \text{ weeks}}{153 \text{ hours}}$ _____
Yes or No

Problem 8g **is** a proportion. This proportion is **not** saying that there are 18 hours in 10 weeks. It might be saying, "I watch 18 hours of TV in 10 weeks."

9. Did you remember to look at the products of the units above?

Answer _____
Yes or No

10. What do you notice about the units on the left-hand side of a proportion as compared to the units on the right-hand side of that same proportion?

_____

_____

11. Use ⬚STO , ⬚EXC , and cross multiplication to decide whether the following are proportions. Write "yes" or "no" on each answer line.

a. $\dfrac{31}{73} \overset{?}{=} \dfrac{1{,}147}{2{,}501}$ _____
Yes or No

b. $\dfrac{31}{73} \overset{?}{=} \dfrac{1{,}147}{2{,}701}$ _____
Yes or No

c. $\dfrac{1{,}470}{270} \overset{?}{=} \dfrac{65}{12}$ _____
Yes or No

d. $\dfrac{65}{12} \overset{?}{=} \dfrac{1{,}462.5}{270}$ _____
Yes or No

e. $\dfrac{2{,}139}{6{,}307} \overset{?}{=} \dfrac{6{,}407}{18{,}921}$ _____
Yes or No

f. $\dfrac{2{,}139}{6{,}407} \overset{?}{=} \dfrac{6{,}417}{19{,}211}$ _____
Yes or No

g. $\dfrac{21.39}{65.13} \overset{?}{=} \dfrac{85.56}{260.52}$ _____
Yes or No

h. $\dfrac{6.153}{85.56} \overset{?}{=} \dfrac{4{,}160}{6{,}307}$ _____
Yes or No

Solving Proportions Using Cross Multiplication

You can use cross multiplication to solve proportions. For example, follow the steps below to solve for *a*.

$$\frac{2}{7} = \frac{6}{a}$$

a. Multiply one set of diagonal numbers. → $2 \times a$

b. Multiply the other diagonal numbers. → 7×6

c. Since the diagonal products are equal, set them equal. → $2 \times a = 7 \times 6$

d. Simplify one side of the equation. → $2 \times a = 42$

1a. What do you do with the 42 and the 2 to solve for *a*? _____

$$\frac{2 \times a}{2} = \frac{42}{2}$$

1b. What is *a*? _____

2. Use diagonal products to solve for *b*.

$$\frac{3}{6} = \frac{5}{b}$$

$$3 \times b = 6 \times 5$$

$$\frac{3 \times b}{3} = \frac{30}{3}$$

$$b = 10$$

The "3 ×" went away because each side was divided by 3.

On one side, *b* is multiplied by 3. To solve for *b*, we must undo the "multiplication by 3" with "division by 3."

What is *b*? _____

     Maneuvers with Fractions

3. Use diagonal products to solve the proportion at the right.

Multiply diagonal numbers.

$$\frac{128}{c} = \frac{7,584}{4,029}$$

$$128 \times 4,029 = c \times 7,584$$

$$\frac{515,712}{7,584} = \frac{c \times 7,584}{7,584}$$ *Simplify.*

$$\frac{515,712}{7,584} = c$$

$c = $ _____

The answer is a whole number.

4. Use cross multiplication to solve the following. Show your work.

$$\frac{13}{25} = \frac{52}{d}$$

$$\frac{13 \times d}{13} = \frac{25 \times 52}{13}$$

$$d = \frac{1,300}{13}$$

$d = $ _____

$$\frac{636}{16} = \frac{e}{184}$$

$$\frac{636 \times 184}{16} = \frac{16 \times e}{16}$$

$$\frac{117,024}{16} = e$$

$e = $ _____

$$\frac{87}{f} = \frac{1,827}{1,953}$$

_____

_____

$f = $ _____

$$\frac{1,251}{g} = \frac{26,271}{273}$$

_____

_____

$g = $ _____

$$\frac{941}{627} = \frac{h}{9,405}$$

_____

_____

$h = $ _____

$$\frac{2,424}{1,212} = \frac{6,262}{j}$$

_____

_____

$j = $ _____

Multiply one diagonal and divide by the remaining number to solve for the unknown.

How Time Flies

1. One in every four years is a leap year with 366 days. Find the average of 366; 365; 365; and 365.

   How many days are in the average year? _____

2. Use proportions to complete the following table.

1 minute	1 hour	1 day	1 year
seconds	**60** minutes	hours	365.25 days
	seconds	minutes	hours
		seconds	minutes
			seconds

3. How old are you? Easy question, right? Maybe not. How old are you in minutes? The answer to this question changes every minute. Find how many minutes old you were on your last birthday. (Do not worry about what time you were born.)

3a. How many years old are you? _____

3b. How many minutes old are you? Show your work.

   Answer _____ minutes

4. How old will you be on your next birthday?

4a. Answer _____ years

4b. Answer _____ minutes

4c. How much older will you be (in minutes)?

   Answer _____ minutes

4d. Does your answer look familiar? _____
   Yes or No

4e. Why? _____

5. Have you ever seen a grandfather clock?
   An essential part of a grandfather clock is the
   pendulum. The *pendulum* is the part that
   swings back and forth and keeps the clock going.
   Build your own pendulum. You will need a
   partner, a watch with a second hand, a pencil,
   a 60 cm piece of string, and something to tie at
   the end of the string like a big nut from a
   "nut and bolt."

   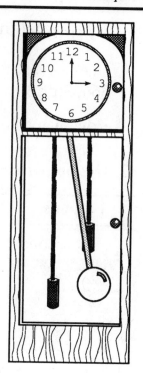

   a. Tie a nut to one end of your string.

   b. Tie the other end of the string to the eraser end
   of a pencil.

   c. Tape the pencil to the edge of a table so that the
   string can swing freely.

   d. Move the nut to one side and then let go.
   Each time the nut swings back to the same side,
   count one complete swing.

6. How many swings does your pendulum make in one minute? Have one
   person count the number of swings and another keep track of the time
   using the watch.

   Number of swings in one minute _____

7a. How many swings would your pendulum make in 5 minutes?

   Answer _____ swings

7b. Write a proportion that shows this.

 8. How many swings would your pendulum make in 1 hour (if it could
   keep going)? Use a proportion and don't forget to use the correct units.

   Answer _____ swings

9. A metronome helps keep time when practicing the piano. It is set to beat 121 times per minute. If it keeps beating this way, how many times will it beat in one day? Show your proportion.

   Answer _____ times

10. On a piano, "A above Middle C" is 440 Hz. This means the piano string vibrates (oscillates) 440 times per second. How many times does it vibrate in 23 seconds? Show your proportion.

   Answer _____ times

11. In the United States, the electricity in household wall sockets is 60 Hertz (60 Hz). Tiny particles called electrons *oscillate* (move back and forth) 60 times per second. (*Hertz* means oscillations per second). Calculate how many oscillations the electric current in your school makes in 11.5 hours using the following proportions.

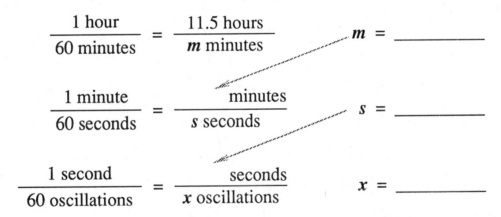

$$\frac{1 \text{ hour}}{60 \text{ minutes}} = \frac{11.5 \text{ hours}}{m \text{ minutes}} \qquad m = \underline{\hspace{2cm}}$$

$$\frac{1 \text{ minute}}{60 \text{ seconds}} = \frac{\text{minutes}}{s \text{ seconds}} \qquad s = \underline{\hspace{2cm}}$$

$$\frac{1 \text{ second}}{60 \text{ oscillations}} = \frac{\text{seconds}}{x \text{ oscillations}} \qquad x = \underline{\hspace{2cm}}$$

12. A radio station that is 720,000 Hz (720 or 72 on the dial), has a carrier wave that oscillates 720,000 times per second. WLS Chicago is 890 on the dial and has a frequency of 890,000 Hz. How many oscillations does the carrier wave of WLS make in 1.5 minutes? Show your work.

   Answer _____ oscillations

Homework 3: It's a Matter of Time

 1. Do not use your calculator in the following problems. If it looks as if it could be a proportion, write "could be" and if it looks like it could not be a proportion, write "crazy." Explain your reasoning.

	Proportion?	Could be or Crazy	Why?
a.	$\dfrac{17}{15} \overset{?}{=} \dfrac{153}{135}$		
b.	$\dfrac{17.2}{14.9} \overset{?}{=} \dfrac{154.8}{134}$		
c.	$\dfrac{0.0002}{0.05} \overset{?}{=} \dfrac{500}{2}$		
d.	$\dfrac{0.0002}{0.05} \overset{?}{=} \dfrac{2}{500}$		
e.	$\dfrac{11 \text{ minutes}}{20 \text{ days}} \overset{?}{=} \dfrac{33 \text{ minutes}}{60 \text{ days}}$		
f.	$\dfrac{19{,}435 \text{ hours}}{58{,}305 \text{ hours}} \overset{?}{=} \dfrac{60 \text{ seconds}}{10 \text{ seconds}}$		
g.	$\dfrac{2 \text{ miles}}{9 \text{ minutes}} \overset{?}{=} \dfrac{18 \text{ miles}}{81 \text{ seconds}}$		
h.	$\dfrac{2 \text{ miles}}{18 \text{ miles}} \overset{?}{=} \dfrac{9 \text{ minutes}}{18 \text{ minutes}}$		

Miss Nishimura's class visited a glass factory that makes empty jars for jelly and peanut butter. Lindy counted finished peanut butter jars for two minutes as they passed by on the conveyor belt. She counted 81 jars.

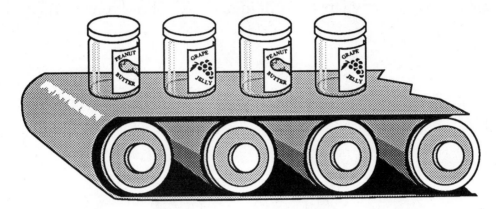

 2. The factory runs for 10 hours each day. How many peanut butter jars do they produce in a day? Start with the following proportion. You will have to write at least one more proportion to solve the problem.

$$\frac{1 \text{ hour}}{60 \text{ minutes}} = \frac{10 \text{ hours}}{x \text{ minutes}}$$

Answer _____ jars

The answer is not 600.

3. At the end of each day, the finished peanut butter jars are sent in cartons to the Jumpy Peanut Butter Company. Each carton holds 480 empty jars. How many cartons does the factory ship in one day? (If a carton is not completely filled, then it is not shipped until the next day.) Use a proportion and show your work.

Answer _____ full cartons

4. Later in the year, Miss Nishimura's class went to the Jammin' Jelly Factory and watched these jars get filled with jelly. They saw that 37 jars were filled in 45 minutes. Jammin' Jelly works an 8.5 hour day. Calculate how many jars they fill in one day. Show your work.

Answer _____ filled jars
Round appropriately.

5. It has been said that, on average, we spend one-third of our lives sleeping. For example, if you are 12 years old, you have spent 4 years of your life sleeping. If you live to be 80 years old, how many years will you sleep? Show your work.

Answer _____ years
R to the nearest tenth.

6. How many days will you spend sleeping? Show your work.

Answer _____ days
R to the nearest day.

4. On Top of the World

Before the construction of a building, a careful **scale model** of the building is made. *"Scale"* means that the model is **proportional** to the actual building. The architects can make their final plans by looking at the scale model.

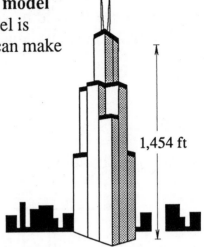

The Sears Tower in Chicago, Illinois is pictured at the right. Since 1974, the Sears Tower has been the tallest building in the world. The Sears Tower has 110 floors and is 1,454 feet high (not including its antennas). In this chapter, assume that each of the floors is the same height.

1,454 ft

At the gift shop in the Sears Tower, you can buy many different-sized scale models of the building. Mr. Levine bought a model of the Sears Tower. Raymond, a student in Mr. Levine's class, measured the model. According to Raymond, the model was 30 cm tall.

Mr. Levine's model and the real building are proportional.

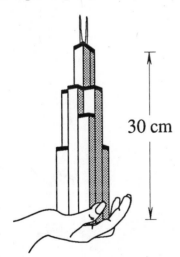

30 cm

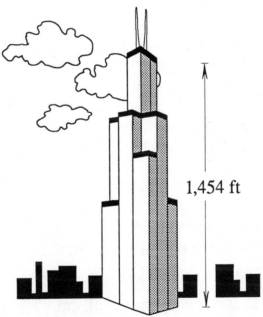

1,454 ft

A **ratio** compares two numbers. The ratio that compares the height of the model and the height of the actual building is 30 cm : 1,454 feet. This ratio can also be written as the following fraction.

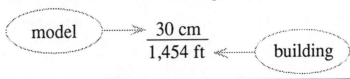

$$\text{model} \dashrightarrow \frac{30 \text{ cm}}{1,454 \text{ ft}} \dashleftarrow \text{building}$$

1a. Raymond looked at the bottom of the model. He noticed that the base of the Sears Tower is a square. The base of the actual Sears Tower is 225 feet on each side. How wide is the base of Mr. Levine's model? Calculate the width, **w**, using the following proportion. Notice a proportion is two equal ratios.

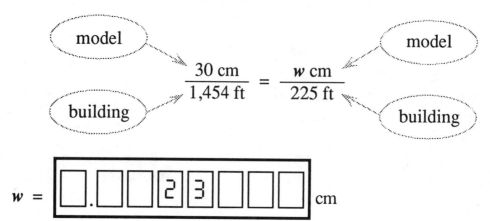

$$\frac{30 \text{ cm}}{1{,}454 \text{ ft}} = \frac{w \text{ cm}}{225 \text{ ft}}$$

w = ☐.☐☐23☐☐☐ cm

1b. Raymond used his ruler to check the calculated measurement for the width of the model's base. What do you think he measured?

Answer _____ cm

2. The Sears Tower is built from nine columns, but there are only four levels. The figure at the right shows the four different levels.

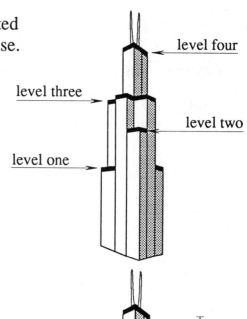

level four

level three

level two

level one

2a. The first level is 661 feet above the ground. Circle the best estimate for the height of the model's first level.

a. Between 0 cm and 10 cm

b. Between 11 cm and 20 cm

c. Between 21 cm and 30 cm

d. More than 30 cm

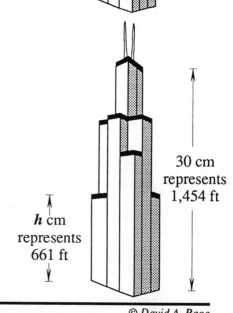

30 cm represents 1,454 ft

h cm represents 661 ft

2b. Complete the following proportion to find the height of the model's first level. Call it **h**. Remember, the total height of the model is 30 cm.

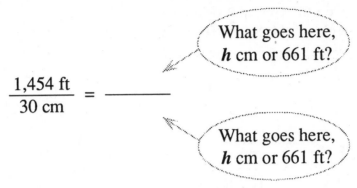

$$\frac{1{,}454 \text{ ft}}{30 \text{ cm}} = \underline{\hspace{2cm}}$$

What goes here, **h** cm or 661 ft?

What goes here, **h** cm or 661 ft?

 2c. Solve for **h**.

h = ☐☐.☐☐☐ 2 3 ☐ cm

2d. Round your answer to make it a practical measurement.

h = _____ cm

R to the nearest tenth.

 3. Blanche measured the height of the model's second level. She said, "The height is 18 cm."

3a. Circle the best estimate for the height of the Sears Tower's second level.

a. Between 0 feet and 500 feet

b. Between 501 feet and 1,000 feet

c. Between 1,001 feet and 1,500 feet

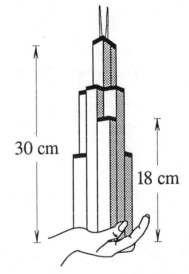
30 cm
18 cm

 3b. Using Blanche's measurement, set up a proportion to find the height of the Sears Tower's second level. Show your proportion and your work.

Height of Sears Tower's second level 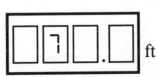 ft

4. When measuring the model, it would be very easy to miss by a millimeter (0.1 cm). Jerry's measurement for the height of the second level was 18.1 cm, not 18 cm. Set up a new proportion using Jerry's measurement to find the height of the Sears Tower's second level.
Show your proportion and your work.

Jerry's answer ⌈ ☐ ☐ 7 . ☐ ⌉ ft

R to the nearest tenth.

5a. Notice the difference between the actual heights of the second level when the measurements were 18 cm and 18.1 cm.

What is the difference between the two actual heights? _____ ft

5b. This means that every 0.1 cm on the model represents _____ feet.

6. The actual height for the second level is 872 feet.
Which model measurement is more accurate?

Answer _____
18 cm or 18.1 cm

7. The third level is 90 floors tall.
Set up a proportion to find the height
of the Sears Tower's third level.

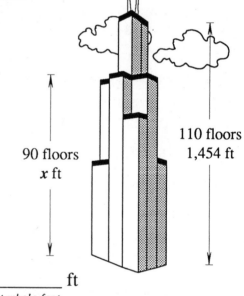

90 floors
x ft

110 floors
1,454 ft

Height of Sears Tower's third level _____ ft
R to the nearest whole foot.

8. Set up a proportion to find the height of the model's third level.

Height of model's third level _____ cm
R to the nearest tenth.

Build Your Own Model of the Sears Tower

Build a model of the Sears Tower using lunch-size milk cartons.
Some directions are given below.

If you could tip the Sears Tower onto its side, you would see that its base is a
large square built from nine smaller squares. The side length of the large square
is 225 feet.

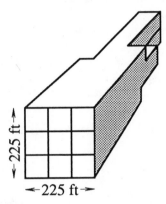

1. What is the side length of each small square? _____ ft

2. The bottom of a milk carton
   is also a square. You will use
   nine milk cartons to build the
   base of your model. Measure
   the base width of one milk carton
   to the nearest 0.1 cm. Write this
   measurement in the following ratio.

_____ cm : 75 feet   *or* $\dfrac{\text{cm}}{75 \text{ feet}}$

3a. Complete the proportion at the right
    to find the height of your scale model.

3b. Solve for *x*.

Answer _____ cm

$\dfrac{\text{cm}}{75 \text{ feet}} = \dfrac{x \text{ cm}}{1,454 \text{ feet}}$

R to the nearest tenth.

4. Complete the following table to determine the heights of your model's four levels. First go back and find the actual height of each level.

Level	Actual Sears Tower in floors	Actual Sears Tower in feet	Your Model in cm *R to the nearest tenth.*
First	50 floors	ft	cm
Second	66 floors	ft	cm
Third	90 floors	ft	cm
Fourth	110 floors	ft	cm

5. How many milk cartons do you think you will need?

   Answer _____

6. Before you begin building your model, unfold the top of each milk carton. Rinse the cartons out with soap and water, and set them aside to dry.

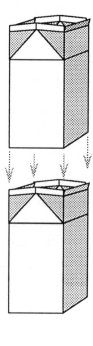

7. Once they are dried, stack the milk cartons to build each column separately, using tape to hold them together. If you open the top of each carton, they will fit inside one another to make a column.

The Sears Tower is built from nine columns: two first-level columns, two second-level columns, three third-level columns, and two fourth-level columns.

one column →

8. After all nine columns are completed, use the steps below to arrange the columns in the correct order. Look at the columns from the top as you tape them together.

1	2	3	4
First Level	Second Level	Third Level	Fourth Level

8a. First, build the north section. Tape a first-level column, a third-level column, and a second-level column next to each other. (The third-level column must be in the middle.) Write "N" on this section.

1	3	2

8b. Build the middle section. Tape a fourth-level column, a fourth-level column, and a third-level column next to each other. (One of the fourth-level columns must be in the middle.) Write "M" on this section.

4	4	3

8c. Build the south section. Tape a second-level column, a third-level column, and a first-level column next to each other. (The third-level column must be in the middle.) Write "S" on this section.

2	3	1

9a. It is time to tape all the sections together. First, tape the north section to the middle section. (The first-level column must touch the fourth-level column.)

1	3	2
4	4	3

9b. Tape the south section to the middle section. (The second-level column must touch a fourth-level column. The first levels should be at diagonally opposite corners.)

1	3	2
4	4	3
2	3	1

If you would like to attach antennas on your model, the Sears Tower has two antennas. They are 253 feet tall.

Homework 4: On Top of the World

1. Find the dimensions of a building in your hometown. Build a model of this building using the same ratio you used for the Sears Tower model. Show your work and draw a sketch of the building.

2. Compare both models. What can you say about the sizes of these buildings?

_____

_____

_____

5. Bits and Pieces

1. The pizza at the right is cut into equal pieces. How many equal pieces are in this pizza?

   Answer _____

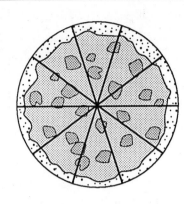

2. The pizza has been cut into **tenths**. Maureen took one piece or $\frac{1}{10}$ (one-tenth) of the pizza. Shade $\frac{1}{10}$ of the pizza.

Look at this fraction more carefully.

The top number is called the *numerator*. The numerator tells how many pieces of pizza Maureen took.

$$\frac{1}{10}$$

The bottom number is called the *denominator*. The denominator tells the total number of equal pieces in the pizza.

3. What fraction of the pizza above is **not** shaded?

How many pieces are not shaded?

How many pieces are in the whole pizza?

4a. How many equal pieces are in the pizza at the right?

   Answer _____

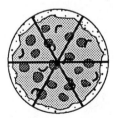

4b. Two pieces are taken away. Circle the fraction which shows how much pizza is left over.

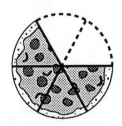

$$\frac{2}{10} \qquad \frac{4}{10} \qquad \frac{2}{6} \qquad \frac{4}{6} \qquad \frac{1}{6}$$

5. Complete the following table. The first row is done for you.

Whole Pizza	Fraction for Whole Pizza	Pieces Taken Away	Fraction of Pizza Taken	Pieces That Are Left	Fraction of Pizza Left
	$\dfrac{12}{12}$		$\dfrac{3}{12}$		$\dfrac{9}{12}$
	$\dfrac{\Box}{\Box}$		$\dfrac{\Box}{\Box}$		$\dfrac{\Box}{\Box}$
	$\dfrac{\Box}{\Box}$		$\dfrac{\Box}{\Box}$		$\dfrac{\Box}{\Box}$
	$\dfrac{\Box}{\Box}$		$\dfrac{\Box}{\Box}$		$\dfrac{\Box}{\Box}$
	$\dfrac{\Box}{\Box}$		$\dfrac{\Box}{\Box}$		$\dfrac{\Box}{\Box}$
	$\dfrac{\Box}{\Box}$		$\dfrac{\Box}{\Box}$		$\dfrac{\Box}{\Box}$

6. What do you notice about all the fractions in the "Fraction for Whole Pizza" column?

7. Complete the following table. The first row is done for you.

	Diagram	What Fraction Is Shaded?	What Fraction Is Unshaded?	Fraction for Whole
a.		$\dfrac{9}{16}$	$\dfrac{7}{16}$	$\dfrac{16}{16}$
b.		$\dfrac{3}{8}$		
c.				
d.				
e.				

8. In the following figure, $\frac{1}{2}$ of the circle is shaded.

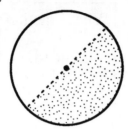

Look at the shading in the following circles. How much is shaded: more than $\frac{1}{2}$, less than $\frac{1}{2}$, or equal to $\frac{1}{2}$?

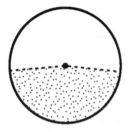   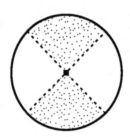   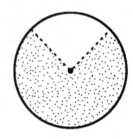

_____   _____   _____
More, Less, or Equal   *More, Less, or Equal*   *More, Less, or Equal*

9. In the following figure, $\frac{4}{6}$ of the rectangle is shaded.

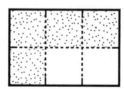

Look at the shading in the following rectangles. How much is shaded: more than $\frac{4}{6}$, less than $\frac{4}{6}$, or equal to $\frac{4}{6}$?

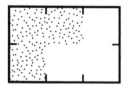   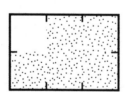   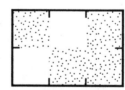   

_____   _____   _____   _____
More, Less, or Equal   *More, Less, or Equal*   *More, Less, or Equal*   *More, Less, or Equal*

10. The rectangles at the right are the same size; however, they are divided differently.

✂ 10a. The top rectangle is divided into fifths. Shade $\frac{3}{5}$ of this rectangle. Then cut out the shaded pieces.

10b. Tape or glue the shaded pieces to make a new rectangle in the space provided below.

11a. The bottom rectangle is divided into tenths. Shade $\frac{6}{10}$ of this rectangle. Then cut out the shaded pieces.

11b. How many tenths did you cut out?

Answer _____

11c. Tape or glue the shaded pieces on top of the rectangle at the right.

12. Which fraction is larger, $\frac{3}{5}$ or $\frac{6}{10}$?

Answer _____

13a. $\frac{3}{5}$ and $\frac{6}{10}$ are equal fractions or *equivalent* fractions. Explain why.

_____

_____

- - - - - - - Cut along line. - - - - - - - -

Tape or glue here.

13b. A proportion says that two fractions are equal. Is $\frac{3}{5} = \frac{6}{10}$ a proportion?

Answer _____
    Yes or No

13c. How could you check? _____

_____

You can compare fractions using pictures like above or using a calculator.

14a. Most scientific calculators cannot show $\frac{3}{5}$ in the window. Instead, these calculators display fractions as **decimal equivalents**.

$\frac{3}{5}$ means 3 ÷ 5.

Press: | 3 | | ÷ | | 5 | | = |

$\frac{3}{5}$ = _____

14b. What is the decimal for $\frac{6}{10}$?

Answer _____

14c. Are the decimals for $\frac{3}{5}$ and $\frac{6}{10}$ equal?

Answer _____

       Yes or No

 15a. What is the decimal for $\frac{4}{9}$?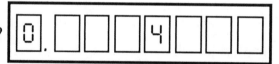

15b. What is the decimal for $\frac{5}{8}$?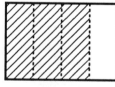

15c. Which fraction is larger, $\frac{4}{9}$ or $\frac{5}{8}$? _____

The longer decimal is **not** always the larger fraction.

Try It Out!

1. Steve and Sylvia have rectangles that are the same size. They shaded their rectangles differently, as shown at the right.

 1a. Steve wanted to divide his rectangle into eighths. Draw a line(s) to divide Steve's rectangle into eighths.

1b. Now what fraction of Steve's rectangle is shaded?

       Answer _____

1c. Does $\frac{3}{4}$ = $\frac{6}{8}$? _____

             Yes or No

1d. How do you know? _____

Steve shaded $\frac{3}{4}$ of his rectangle.

Sylvia shaded $\frac{6}{8}$ of her rectangle.

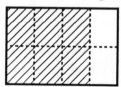

2a. Shade $\frac{16}{24}$ of the rectangle below.   2b. Shade $\frac{8}{12}$ of the rectangle below.

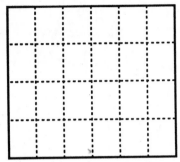   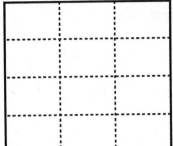

2c. Does $\frac{16}{24}$ = $\frac{8}{12}$? _____

Yes or No

2d. How do you know? _____

2e. If the answer to Problem 2c is "No," which fraction is larger? _____

3a. Shade $\frac{5}{6}$ of the rectangle below.   3b. Shade $\frac{13}{16}$ of the rectangle below.

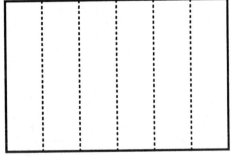   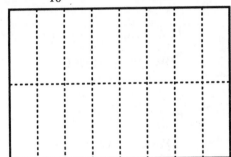

3c. Does $\frac{5}{6}$ = $\frac{13}{16}$? _____

Yes or No

3d. If the answer to Problem 3c is "No," which fraction is larger? _____

  4a. Shade $\frac{5}{9}$ of the rectangle below.   4b. Shade $\frac{5}{18}$ of the rectangle below.
First divide the rectangle into eighteenths.

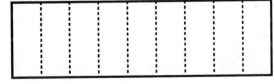   

4c. Does $\frac{5}{9}$ = $\frac{5}{18}$? _____

Yes or No

4d. If the answer to Problem 4c is "No," which fraction is larger? _____

5. Is $\frac{15}{25} = \frac{6}{10}$ a proportion? To decide, solve this problem two ways.

5a. **First Way:**

5b. **Second Way:**

5c. Does $\frac{15}{25} = \frac{6}{10}$? _____

Yes or No

 6. Are the following fractions equivalent (equal)?

a. $\frac{8}{24} \overset{?}{=} \frac{4}{12}$ _____

Yes or No

How did you decide? _____

b. $\frac{4}{12} \overset{?}{=} \frac{2}{6}$ _____

Yes or No

How did you decide? _____

c. $\frac{2}{6} \overset{?}{=} \frac{1}{3}$ _____

Yes or No

How did you decide? _____

7. The following four rectangles are the same size. Each rectangle has a fraction from Problem 6 written underneath it. Shade the rectangles to show each of these fractions. The first one is done for you.

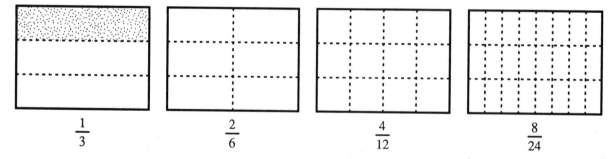

8. What happened to the numerator and the denominator from one rectangle to the next?

_____

9. Are all the fractions in Problem 7 equivalent? _____

Yes or No

We Are Family!

1. A *fraction family* is a group of equal fractions. The following fractions belong to the same family. The entire family could never be written because there is an infinite number of members.

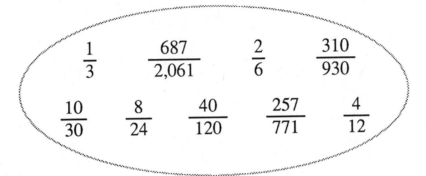

 What is the decimal equivalent for all of the members above?

Answer: $0.\boxed{}\,\boxed{}\,\boxed{}\,\boxed{3}\,\boxed{}\,\boxed{}\,\boxed{}$

If you multiply both the numerator **and** the denominator of a fraction by the **same** number, you get another fraction in that family.

Example 1: $\dfrac{1}{3} = \dfrac{1 \times 5}{3 \times 5} = \dfrac{5}{15}$

Example 2: $\dfrac{4}{12} = \dfrac{4 \times 3}{12 \times 3} = \dfrac{12}{36}$

Example 3: $\dfrac{8}{24} = \dfrac{8 \times 10}{24 \times 10} = \dfrac{80}{240}$

$\dfrac{5}{15}$, $\dfrac{12}{36}$, and $\dfrac{80}{240}$ are three more members of the fraction family above.

---

2. Write two more fractions that belong to the family above.

Answers _____ and _____

---

3. Mallory wrote $\frac{3}{9}$ and $\frac{783,498}{2,350,494}$ for Problem 2.

$$\frac{783,498}{2,350,494} \quad \text{looks} \quad \text{BIG}$$

$$\frac{3}{9} \quad \text{looks} \quad \text{small}$$

Nancy said, "Could these two fractions be equal?" You decide. Show your work.

$$\frac{3}{9} \overset{?}{=} \frac{783,498}{2,350,494}$$

Answer _____
              Yes or No

Of all the fractions in this huge family, $\frac{1}{3}$ is the simplest member. The simplest family member is in lowest terms. ***Lowest terms*** means you **cannot** write an equal fraction with a smaller numerator and denominator, using whole numbers.

4. Fill in the boxes.

$$\frac{1}{3} = \frac{100}{\boxed{}} = \frac{\boxed{}}{99} = \frac{103}{\boxed{}} = \frac{\boxed{}}{90} = \frac{250}{\boxed{}}$$

5. The following rectangles are the same size. Use the rectangles to show a new fraction family. Each fraction must be equivalent but different. Shade and label each rectangle.

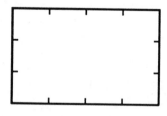 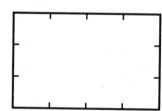 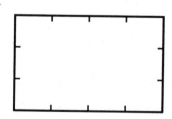

_____   _____   _____

The rectangles on this page are the same size.

6a. What fraction is shaded at the right?

Answer _____

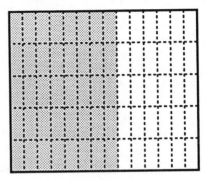

6b. What fraction is shaded at the right?

Answer _____

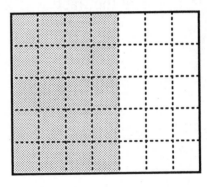

6c. Are the fractions above in the same fraction family?

Answer _____
        Yes or No

6d. How did you decide? _____

6e. What fraction is shaded at the right?

Answer _____

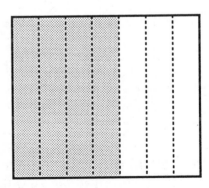

6f. Is this fraction in the same fraction family as the two above?

Answer _____
        Yes or No

6g. How did you decide? _____

7. How do you find the simplest member in a fraction family?
   Look at the fractions $\frac{40}{70}$ and $\frac{20}{35}$.

$$\frac{40}{70} = \frac{20}{35} \qquad\qquad 40 : 70 :: 20 : 35$$

What was done to the left side to get the right side? _____

_____

8. Look at the fractions $\frac{20}{35}$ and $\frac{4}{7}$.

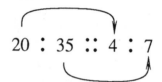

$$\frac{20}{35} = \frac{4}{7} \qquad\qquad 20 : 35 :: 4 : 7$$

What was done to the left side to get the right side? _____

_____

9. Look at the fractions $\frac{40}{70}$ and $\frac{4}{7}$.

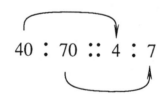

$$\frac{40}{70} = \frac{4}{7} \qquad\qquad 40 : 70 :: 4 : 7$$

What was done to the left side to get the right side? _____

_____

10. Which operation ($+, -, \times, \div$) do you use to get a fraction in lower terms?

    Answer _____

11a. List all the whole numbers that will divide evenly into both 40 and 70. A number divides evenly if there is no remainder.

    Answer _____

11b. These numbers are **common factors** of 40 and 70. What is the largest common factor for 40 and 70?

    Answer _____

If you divide the numerator **and** denominator of a fraction by a common factor, you get another fraction in that family. If you divide the numerator and denominator by the **largest** common factor, you get the member that is in lowest terms.

Example 1: Start with $\frac{24}{36}$.

Since 3 is a common factor of 24 and 36, divide the top and the bottom by 3.

$$\frac{24}{36} = \frac{24 \div 3}{36 \div 3} = \frac{8}{12} \qquad \frac{8}{12} = \frac{24}{36}$$

Example 2: Start with $\frac{24}{36}$.

Since 12 is the largest common factor of 24 and 36, divide the top and the bottom by 12 to get the member that is in lowest terms.

$$\frac{24}{36} = \frac{24 \div 12}{36 \div 12} = \frac{2}{3} \qquad \frac{2}{3} = \frac{24}{36}$$

12a. Start with $\frac{48}{84}$. Since 2 is a factor of 48 and 84, divide the numerator and denominator by 2.

$$\frac{48}{84} = \frac{48 \div 2}{84 \div 2} = \frac{\boxed{}}{\boxed{}}$$

$\frac{48}{84}$ and $\frac{24}{42}$ are equivalent. The numerator and denominator were **reduced** to **lower** terms. The reduced fraction is **not** a smaller number.

12b. Divide both the numerator and denominator of $\frac{24}{42}$ by 2.

What is your new fraction? _____

12c. What number divides evenly into the new numerator and denominator in Problem 12b?

Answer _____

12d. Reduce the fraction one more time. _____

This is the member of the family that is in **lowest** terms. The new numerator and denominator do not have another factor in common.

Try It Out Again!

   1. Reduce $\frac{75}{175}$ to lowest terms. Leave a trail of your work.

Answer _____

2a. Reduce $\frac{224}{616}$ to lowest terms. Leave a trail of your work.

Answer _____

2b. Check to see if $\frac{224}{616}$ and your answer to Problem 2a are equal. If they are not, go back and find your mistake.

$\frac{224}{616} =$ _____ is a proportion.
        <small>*Answer to Problem 2a*</small>

3. Reduce the following fractions to lowest terms. Make sure your statement is a proportion.

   a. $\frac{30}{66} =$ _____   What did you divide by? _____

   b. $\frac{44}{66} =$ _____   What did you divide by? _____

   c. $\frac{144}{176} =$ _____   What did you divide by? _____

   d. $\frac{300}{500} =$ _____   What did you divide by? _____

   e. $\frac{189}{378} =$ _____   What did you divide by? _____

4a. The following list includes 9 members from a fraction family.
   Find the fraction that does not belong to this family. Cross it out.

$$\frac{8}{10} \qquad \frac{40}{50} \qquad \frac{300}{375} \qquad \frac{312}{370} \qquad \frac{80}{100}$$

$$\frac{12}{15} \qquad \frac{16}{20} \qquad \frac{4}{5} \qquad \frac{48}{60} \qquad \frac{20}{25}$$

4b. Explain how you decided which fraction did not belong. _____

_____

4c. Put a loop around the member of the family above that is in lowest terms.

5a. The following list includes 9 members from a fraction family.
   Find the fraction that does not belong to this family. Cross it out.

$$\frac{34}{51} \qquad \frac{18}{27} \qquad \frac{2}{3} \qquad \frac{1,196}{1,794} \qquad \frac{38}{57}$$

$$\frac{3}{5} \qquad \frac{4}{6} \qquad \frac{1,198}{1,797} \qquad \frac{9,174}{13,761} \qquad \frac{22}{33}$$

5b. Put a loop around the member of the family above that is in lowest terms.

6a. The following list includes 9 members from a fraction family.
   Find the fraction that does not belong to this family. Cross it out.

$$\frac{6}{21} \qquad \frac{4}{14} \qquad \frac{200}{700} \qquad \frac{201}{700} \qquad \frac{202}{707}$$

$$\frac{10}{35} \qquad \frac{12}{42} \qquad \frac{2}{7} \qquad \frac{16}{56} \qquad \frac{32}{112}$$

6b. Put a loop around the member of the family above that is in lowest terms.

Homework 5: Bits and Pieces

1. The rectangle at the right is cut into equal pieces.

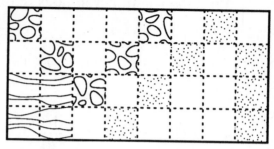

1a. What fraction of the rectangle is shaded  ? _____

1b. What fraction of the rectangle is shaded  ? _____

1c. What fraction of the rectangle is shaded  ? _____

1d. What fraction of the rectangle is shaded  ? _____

2. Manuel had a rectangle.

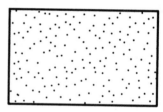

He cut it into four pieces as shown at the right.

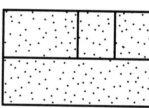

He took out this piece.

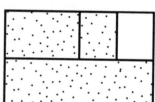

Manuel said, "I cut the rectangle into four pieces and took one piece. So the piece I took is one-fourth ($\frac{1}{4}$) of the rectangle."

2a. How would you convince Manuel that his statement is not correct?

_____

2b. Which fraction best describes the piece Manuel took? Circle the answer at the right. $\frac{1}{2}$ $\frac{1}{4}$ $\frac{1}{8}$ $\frac{1}{16}$

3. Each of the eight students in the math club has four pens. Answer the following questions. Reduce your answers to lowest terms if possible.

3a. How many pens do they have altogether? _____

3b. Eight of the pens are black. What fraction is black? _____

3c. Ten of the pens are blue. What fraction is blue? _____

3d. Four of the pens are green. What fraction is green? _____

3e. Six of the pens are red. What fraction is red? _____

3f. The rest of the pens ran out of ink. How many pens ran out of ink?

   Answer _____

4. The following picture shows a flock of twenty sheep in a field.

4a. Divide the sheep into 5 equal groups.

   How many sheep are in each group? _____

4b. One-fifth ($\frac{1}{5}$) of the sheep was put in a truck.

   How many sheep are in the truck? _____

4c. One-half ($\frac{1}{2}$) of the original flock was put in a pen.

   How many sheep are in the pen? _____

4d. One-fourth ($\frac{1}{4}$) of the original flock of sheep was put into a barn.
   Hint: Think about dividing the flock into 4 equal groups.

   How many sheep are in the barn? _____

4e. How many sheep are left in the field? _____

4f. What fraction of the flock is left in the field? _____

5. The following picture shows a flock of 45 birds.

5a. $\frac{33}{45}$ of the flock decides to fly south. Put a loop around $\frac{33}{45}$ of the flock.

5b. Reduce $\frac{33}{45}$ to lowest terms. _____

5c. $\frac{2}{9}$ of the original flock decides to fly west. Put a loop around $\frac{2}{9}$ of the flock.

5d. How many birds are not in these two groups? _____

5e. What fraction of the birds is in neither of these two groups?

Answer _____

6. The Slammin' Company produced 150 basketballs. $\frac{1}{5}$ of the basketballs was shipped to the Chicago Bulls. $\frac{1}{3}$ of the basketballs was shipped to the Los Angeles Lakers. $\frac{1}{15}$ was shipped to the Detroit Pistons. Sixty basketballs were shipped to the New York Knicks.

6a. How many basketballs were shipped to the Bulls? _____

6b. How many basketballs were shipped to the Lakers? _____

6c. How many basketballs were shipped to the Pistons? _____

6d. In lowest terms, what fraction of the basketballs was shipped to the Knicks?

Answer _____

6. How to Be Smarter Than Your Calculator

 1. Circle your best guess for the following questions.

1a. Which fraction is **largest**?

$$\frac{1}{2} \qquad \frac{1}{3} \qquad \frac{1}{4} \qquad \frac{1}{5} \qquad \frac{1}{10}$$

1b. Which fraction is **largest**?

$$\frac{1}{10} \qquad \frac{2}{10} \qquad \frac{5}{10} \qquad \frac{7}{10} \qquad \frac{9}{10}$$

1c. Which fraction is **smallest**?

$$\frac{1}{2} \qquad \frac{1}{3} \qquad \frac{1}{4} \qquad \frac{1}{5} \qquad \frac{1}{10}$$

1d. Which fraction is **smallest**?

$$\frac{1}{10} \qquad \frac{2}{10} \qquad \frac{5}{10} \qquad \frac{7}{10} \qquad \frac{9}{10}$$

 2. Shade the fractions and write their decimal equivalents in the table.

	Fraction	Fraction Shaded	Decimal Equivalent *Copy window.*
a.	$\frac{1}{2}$		
b.	$\frac{1}{3}$		
c.	$\frac{1}{4}$		
d.	$\frac{1}{5}$		
e.	$\frac{1}{10}$		

Maneuvers with Fractions

3. Use the decimal equivalents from the table on page 75 to answer the following questions.

3a. Which fraction is largest? Check your answer with your guess in Problem 1a. $\frac{1}{2}$ $\frac{1}{3}$ $\frac{1}{4}$ $\frac{1}{5}$ $\frac{1}{10}$

3b. When the numerator stays the same and the denominator gets larger, what happens to the size of the fraction?

_____

3c. Why? _____

4a. Which fraction is largest? $\frac{1}{10}$ $\frac{2}{10}$ $\frac{5}{10}$ $\frac{7}{10}$ $\frac{9}{10}$

4b. When the denominator stays the same and the numerator gets larger, what happens to the size of the fraction?

_____

4c. Why? _____

5a. Which fraction is largest: $\frac{1}{8,888,889}$, $\frac{1}{8,888,888}$, or $\frac{1}{8,888,887}$? _____

5b. Explain. _____

6. Complete the following table.

	Fraction	Decimal Equivalent *Copy window.*
a.	$\frac{1}{8,888,889}$	
b.	$\frac{1}{8,888,888}$	
c.	$\frac{1}{8,888,887}$	

7. According to the calculator, which decimal is the largest:

$\frac{1}{8,888,889}$, $\frac{1}{8,888,888}$, or $\frac{1}{8,888,887}$? _____

(You are **smarter** than your calculator!)

$\frac{1}{2}$ and 0.5 are equally accurate. However, $\frac{1}{3}$ and 0.3333333 are **not** equally accurate. If the calculator had more window space, it would show more 3's. This pattern continues forever and the calculator cannot give an exact decimal equivalent.

$$\frac{1}{3} = .3333\overset{33333^{3333^{3}}\cdots}{}$$

8a. What is the decimal equivalent for $\frac{2}{3}$? _____
    Copy window.

8b. What number goes on forever? _____

8c. Why is the last digit in the calculator window a "7"? _____

9a. What is the decimal equivalent for $\frac{13}{99}$? _____
    Copy window.

9b. Sometimes you can guess how the decimal continues. If your calculator had 16 digits of window space, guess the decimal equivalent for $\frac{13}{99}$.

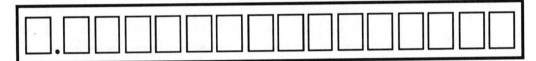

10. A computer shows the first sixty-five digits of the decimal equivalent for $\frac{5}{17}$; however, this decimal fraction repeats forever. Circle the pattern (repeating block) in the computer's answer that follows.

0.29411764705882352941176470588235294117647058823529411764705882235

The calculator cannot always give an exact answer. For example, to add $\frac{2}{17}$ and $\frac{5}{17}$ accurately, we need to work with fractions.

11. The rectangle below is divided into 17 equal pieces.

11a. Shade $\frac{2}{17}$ of the rectangle using a red pen.

11b. Shade $\frac{5}{17}$ of the rectangle using a blue pen. Do not shade over the red.

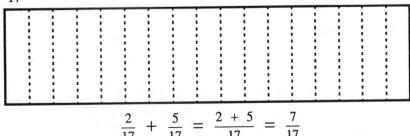

$$\frac{2}{17} + \frac{5}{17} = \frac{2+5}{17} = \frac{7}{17}$$

Maneuvers with Fractions

12. The circle at the right is divided into 9 equal pieces. Use the circle to find the sum of $\frac{2}{9}$ + $\frac{5}{9}$.

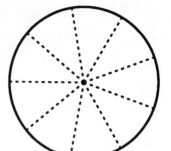

12a. Shade $\frac{2}{9}$ of the circle using a red pen.

12b. Shade $\frac{5}{9}$ of the circle using a blue pen.

12c. $\frac{2}{9}$ + $\frac{5}{9}$ = _____

12d. Bob's answer for Problem 12c was $\frac{7}{18}$. How would you help Bob correct his mistake?

_____

13. The following rectangle is divided into 24 equal pieces. Use the rectangle to find the sum of $\frac{14}{24}$ + $\frac{9}{24}$.

13a. Shade $\frac{14}{24}$ of the rectangle using a red pen.

13b. Shade $\frac{9}{24}$ of the rectangle using a blue pen.

13c. $\frac{14}{24}$ + $\frac{9}{24}$ = _____

Take It Away

 1a. Divide the following rectangle into seven equal pieces.

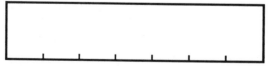

1b. Lightly shade 6 pieces using a **pencil**.

1c. What fraction is shaded? _____

1d. Erase 2 of the pieces you shaded.

1e. What fraction did you erase? _____

1f. What fraction is still shaded? _____

1g. $\frac{6}{7}$ − $\frac{2}{7}$ = _____

2a. Divide the following rectangle into 13 equal pieces.

2b. Lightly shade 11 pieces using a pencil.

2c. What fraction is shaded? _____

2d. Erase 5 of the pieces you shaded.

2e. What fraction did you erase? _____

2f. What fraction is still shaded? _____

2g. What subtraction problem did you just do?

$$\frac{\boxed{}}{\boxed{}} - \frac{\boxed{}}{\boxed{}} = \frac{\boxed{}}{\boxed{}}$$

3a. How many thirteenths are there in 1? _____

3b. What is $1 - \frac{6}{13}$? _____

4. The following bar is divided into 14 equal pieces.

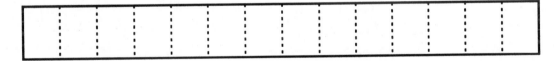

4a. Shade 4 pieces red, 3 pieces blue, and 5 pieces green.

4b. What is $\frac{4}{14} + \frac{3}{14} + \frac{5}{14}$? _____
Do not reduce.

4c. How many fourteenths are in 1? _____

4d. What is $1 - \frac{12}{14}$? _____

4e. Reduce your answer to lowest terms. _____

When the denominators (bottoms) of two fractions are the same, both fractions are built from the same size pieces. When the denominators of two fractions are the same, they have **common denominators**.

In $\frac{14}{24} + \frac{9}{24}$, the number 24, is called a common denominator. This is just another name for "same denominator."

To add or subtract two (or more) fractions with a common denominator, just add or subtract the numerators and keep the common denominator.

5. In the following problems, if the denominators are not equal, write "no common denominator." If there is a common denominator, add or subtract the fractions. Do not reduce your answers. If too much is subtracted, write "less than zero." The first few are done for you.

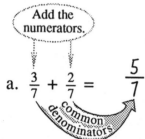

a. $\frac{3}{7} + \frac{2}{7} = \frac{5}{7}$

b. $\frac{3}{7} - \frac{5}{7} =$ less than zero

c. $\frac{3}{20} + \frac{4}{30} =$ no common denominator

d. $\frac{5}{7} - \frac{3}{7} = \frac{2}{7}$

e. $\frac{19}{43} + \frac{11}{43} =$

f. $\frac{3}{5} + \frac{2}{5} =$

g. $\frac{3}{7} - \frac{5}{8} =$

h. $\frac{3}{820} + \frac{17}{820} =$

j. $\frac{17}{820} - \frac{3}{820} =$

k. $\frac{3}{825} - \frac{17}{825} =$

m. $\frac{3}{825} - \frac{1}{825} =$

n. $\frac{6}{1,234} + \frac{5}{12,345} =$

p. $\frac{1,000}{12,345} - \frac{900}{12,345} =$

q. $\frac{209}{1,000,000} - \frac{201}{1,000,000} =$

What Do You Have in Common?

1a. Use a blue pen to shade $\frac{5}{14}$ of the following rectangle.

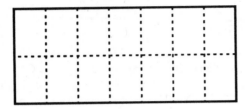

1b. Use a red pen to shade $\frac{3}{7}$ of the following rectangle.

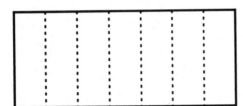

1c. Draw a line(s) in the second rectangle so it is divided into 14 equal pieces.

1d. How many fourteenths are shaded in the second rectangle?

Answer _____

1e. Using the rectangles, add $\frac{5}{14}$ and $\frac{3}{7}$.

$$\frac{5}{14} = \frac{5}{14}$$

$$+ \frac{3}{7} = \frac{\boxed{}}{14}$$

$$\frac{\boxed{}}{\boxed{}}$$

1f. What is the common denominator for this problem?

Answer _____

2a. Michelle wrote $\frac{5}{14} + \frac{3}{7} = \frac{8}{21}$. What did Michelle do wrong?

_____

2b. Vance wrote $\frac{5}{14} + \frac{3}{7} = \frac{11}{28}$. What did Vance do wrong?

_____

3a. Is $\frac{5}{14} + \frac{3}{7}$ greater than, less than, or equal to 1? _____

Greater, Less, or Equal

3b. What is $\frac{5}{14} + \frac{3}{7} + \frac{3}{14}$? _____

3c. Is $\frac{5}{14} + \frac{3}{7} + \frac{5}{14}$ greater than, less than, or equal to 1? _____

Greater, Less, or Equal

4a. A common denominator for $\frac{5}{16} + \frac{3}{8}$ is 16. What fraction is equal to $\frac{3}{8}$ and has a denominator of 16?

Solve the proportion $\frac{3}{8} = \frac{x}{16}$.

$$\frac{3}{8} = \frac{\boxed{}}{16}$$

4b. Shade the following rectangle to find the sum of $\frac{5}{16} + \frac{3}{8}$.

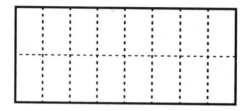

$$\frac{5}{16} + \frac{\boxed{}}{16} = \frac{\boxed{}}{\boxed{}}$$

5. A common denominator for $\frac{5}{7} + \frac{3}{14}$ is 14. What fraction is equal to $\frac{5}{7}$ and has a denominator of 14?

5a. Solve the proportion $\frac{5}{7} = \frac{a}{14}$.

$$\frac{5}{7} = \frac{\boxed{}}{14}$$

The following rectangle is divided into 14 equal pieces. Use the rectangle and the steps below to find the sum of $\frac{5}{7} + \frac{3}{14}$.

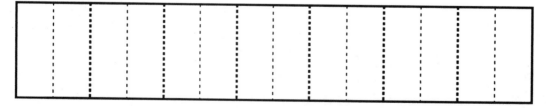

5b. Shade $\frac{5}{7}$ of the rectangle using a colored pen.

5c. Shade $\frac{3}{14}$ of the rectangle using a different color.

5d. $\frac{5}{7} + \frac{3}{14} =$ _____

6a. Add $\frac{1}{5} + \frac{7}{15}$ using the following steps. The common denominator is 15.

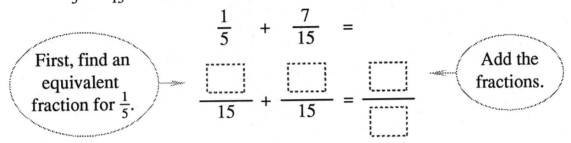

First, find an equivalent fraction for $\frac{1}{5}$.

$$\frac{1}{5} + \frac{7}{15} =$$

$$\frac{\square}{15} + \frac{\square}{15} = \frac{\square}{\square}$$

Add the fractions.

6b. Reduce your answer to lowest terms. _____

7. The following rectangle is divided into 4 equal pieces.

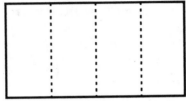

7a. Lightly shade $\frac{3}{4}$ of the rectangle with a pencil.

 7b. Draw line(s) to divide the rectangle into 8 equal pieces.

7c. How many pieces are shaded now? _____

7d. What fraction is shaded now? _____

7e. Erase one piece. What fraction did you erase? _____

7f. What fraction is shaded now? _____

7g. You just did the following subtraction problem.

$$\frac{3}{4} - \frac{1}{8} = \frac{\square}{8} - \frac{\square}{8} = \frac{\square}{8}$$

First, you found a common denominator and renamed one of the fractions. Then you subtracted the numerators.

8. Subtract $\frac{4}{7} - \frac{1}{42}$. The common denominator is 42.

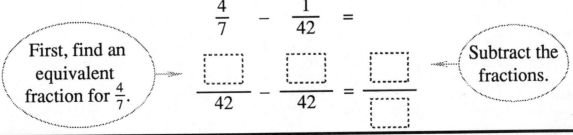

$$\frac{4}{7} - \frac{1}{42} =$$

First, find an equivalent fraction for $\frac{4}{7}$.

$$\frac{\square}{42} - \frac{\square}{42} = \frac{\square}{\square}$$

Subtract the fractions.

9. Subtract $\frac{34}{51} - \frac{1}{3}$. The common denominator is 51.

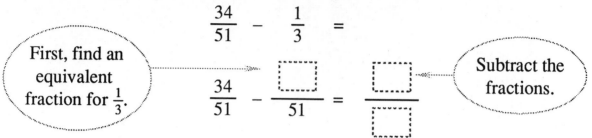

$$\frac{34}{51} - \frac{1}{3} =$$

$$\frac{34}{51} - \frac{\boxed{}}{51} = \frac{\boxed{}}{\boxed{}}$$

First, find an equivalent fraction for $\frac{1}{3}$.

Subtract the fractions.

10. Add or subtract the following fractions after you find a common denominator. Hint: Only one denominator will have to be renamed in each problem. Leave a trail of your work. Do not reduce your answers. If too much is subtracted, write "less than zero."

a. $\frac{1}{2} + \frac{3}{8} =$

b. $\frac{1}{2} - \frac{3}{8} =$

c. $\frac{2}{3} + \frac{1}{9} =$

d. $\frac{1}{9} - \frac{2}{3} =$

e. $\frac{3}{8} + \frac{5}{56} =$

f. $\frac{3}{8} + \frac{10}{56} =$

g. $\frac{25}{56} - \frac{3}{8} =$

h. $\frac{30}{56} - \frac{4}{7} =$

j. $\frac{35}{56} - \frac{6}{7} =$

k. $\frac{109}{1,000} + \frac{4}{5} =$

m. $\frac{4}{5} - \frac{109}{1,000} =$

n. $\frac{3}{11} - \frac{1}{110} =$

p. $\frac{147}{555} + \frac{32}{111} =$

q. $\frac{147}{555} - \frac{32}{111} =$

r. $\frac{1}{20} + \frac{3}{100} =$

s. $\frac{1}{20} - \frac{3}{100} =$

In the previous exercises, you only had to change one denominator.
Sometimes you will have to change both denominators.

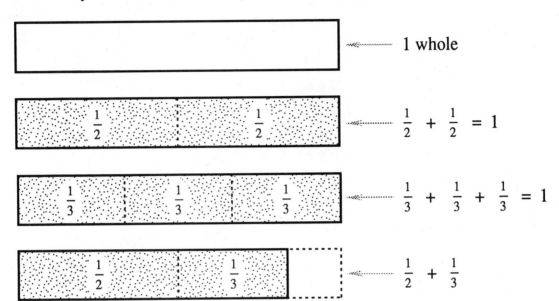

11a. Is $\frac{1}{2} + \frac{1}{3}$ more or less than 1? _____
                                                    More or Less

11b. To add $\frac{1}{2}$ and $\frac{1}{3}$, you need to cut the whole rectangle into smaller pieces.
     Sixths will work.

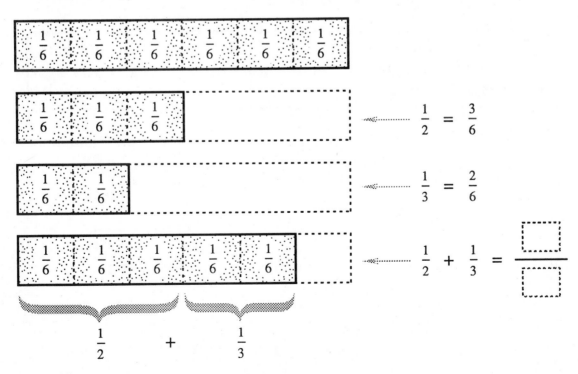

Before you add $\frac{1}{6} + \frac{3}{8}$, you need a common denominator. 48 is one possibility because

$$6 \times 8 = 48;$$

therefore,

$$48 \div 6 = 8$$

and

$$48 \div 8 = 6.$$

12. Add $\frac{1}{6} + \frac{3}{8}$ using the following steps.

12a. First solve the proportions.

12b. Now that you have common
denominators, add the fractions.

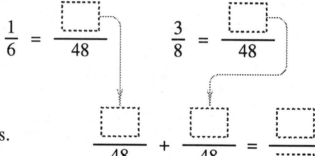

12c. Reduce your answer to lowest terms. _____

> We found a common denominator by multiplying the denominators, 6 and 8. **Multiplying the denominators will always give you a common denominator.**

13a. Sometimes you can find a smaller common denominator. The number 24 is also a common denominator for the fractions $\frac{1}{6}$ and $\frac{3}{8}$.

$$\frac{1}{6} = \frac{\boxed{}}{24} \qquad\qquad \frac{3}{8} = \frac{\boxed{}}{24}$$

13b. Now that you have common denominators, add the fractions.

$$\frac{\boxed{}}{24} + \frac{\boxed{}}{24} = \underline{\qquad\qquad\qquad}$$

Should agree with Problem 12c.

14. The fractions, $\frac{5}{6}$ and $\frac{1}{9}$, have different denominators.

14a. **Multiply** the denominators to find a common denominator. Fill in the common denominator in the following boxes.

$$\frac{5}{6} = \frac{}{\boxed{}} \qquad\qquad \frac{1}{9} = \frac{}{\boxed{}}$$

14b. Now write in the new numerators above.

14c. Add the fractions and reduce your answer to lowest terms. _____

15. Another common denominator for $\frac{5}{6}$ and $\frac{1}{9}$ is 36.

15a. What is a common denominator for $\frac{5}{6}$ and $\frac{1}{9}$ that is lower than 36?

   Answer _____

15b. Add the fractions using this common denominator. Reduce, if possible.

$$\frac{5}{6} = \frac{\boxed{}}{\boxed{}} \qquad\qquad \frac{1}{9} = \frac{\boxed{}}{\boxed{}}$$

   Answer _____

   Compare with Problem 14c.

16. Add or subtract the following fractions and reduce your answers to lowest terms. Leave a trail of your work. Remember, the product of the denominators always gives a common denominator. A smaller common denominator is a little easier to work with, if you can find it.

   a. $\frac{4}{9} + \frac{3}{10} =$ 　　　　　　　　b. $\frac{2}{3} - \frac{1}{5} =$

   c. $\frac{3}{7} + \frac{2}{5} =$ 　　　　　　　　d. $\frac{7}{16} + \frac{5}{12} =$

   e. $\frac{3}{11} - \frac{3}{13} =$ 　　　　　　　　f. $\frac{5}{12} + \frac{11}{20} =$

   g. $\frac{4}{21} - \frac{4}{23} =$ 　　　　　　　　h. $\frac{14}{25} - \frac{16}{75} =$

Homework 6: How to Be Smarter Than Your Calculator

1. The square at the right is
   divided into 16 equal pieces.

1a. Shade $\frac{1}{2}$ of the square red.

1b. Shade another $\frac{1}{4}$ of the square blue.

1c. $\frac{1}{2} + \frac{1}{4} =$ _____

1d. What fraction is not shaded? _____

1e. Shade another $\frac{1}{8}$ of the square with a different color.

1f. $\frac{1}{2} + \frac{1}{4} + \frac{1}{8} =$ _____

1g. What fraction is not shaded? _____

1h. Shade $\frac{1}{16}$ of the square with a fourth color.

1j. $\frac{1}{2} + \frac{1}{4} + \frac{1}{8} + \frac{1}{16} =$ _____

1k. What fraction is not shaded? _____

1m. What pattern(s) do you see with the problems above?

_____

1n. What is the next addition problem in the pattern? _____

2. Write "Greater," "Less," or "Equal" on the following answer lines.

   a. $\frac{9}{10} - \frac{3}{10}$ is _____ than $\frac{1}{2}$.

Greater, Less, or Equal

   b. $\frac{2}{3} + \frac{2}{3}$ is _____ than 1.

Greater, Less, or Equal

   c. $\frac{1}{11} + \frac{1}{11} + \frac{1}{11} + \frac{1}{11} + \frac{1}{11}$ is _____ than $\frac{1}{2}$.

Greater, Less, or Equal

3a. Tim Jackson scored $\frac{3}{7}$ of his basketball team's points. His friend, Roberto Cruz, scored $\frac{2}{7}$ of the points. Together, what fraction of the total points did they score? Show your work.

Answer _____

3b. Did they score more or less than $\frac{1}{2}$ of the total points?

Answer _____
More   or   Less

4. Carlos, Tim, and Donnell shot 42 out of their team's 60 free-throw attempts. Carlos and Tim shot a total of 30 free-throw attempts. What fraction of the team's attempts did Donnell shoot?

Answer _____

5. During the 1992 NBA All Star Game, $\frac{90}{153}$ of the points were scored by the Western Conference Starting Team. What fraction of the points were scored by the rest of the team?

Answer _____

6. In this game, Chris Mullin missed $\frac{1}{7}$ of the field goals he attempted. What fraction did he make?

Answer _____

7a. In this game, Magic Johnson made 12 field-goal attempts. Nine of these attempts went in the basket. What fraction did Magic Johnson make?

Answer _____

7b. What fraction did he miss? _____

8. Darlene Linton scored $\frac{1}{5}$ of the points in her basketball game. Her friend, Whitney White, scored $\frac{3}{20}$ of the points.

8a. Before calculating, do you think Darlene and Whitney scored more or less than half of their team's points in the game?

Answer _____
           More or Less

8b. Who scored more points, Darlene or Whitney? _____
                                        Darlene or Whitney

8c. Calculate the fraction of points scored by Darlene and Whitney.

Answer _____

9a. Calisha, Sandra, and Jamie were on a team in a free-throw contest. Calisha scored $\frac{5}{12}$ of the free throws, Sandra scored $\frac{1}{3}$ of the free throws, and Jamie scored $\frac{1}{4}$ of the free throws. What fraction of the team's free throws was scored by these three girls?

Answer _____

9b. Did anyone else on their team score a free throw? _____
                                          Yes or No

9c. How do you know? _____

10. The Patriots of Lincoln School won the basketball championship against the Tigers of Jackson School. Charles Anderson scored $\frac{1}{3}$, Rigo Salgado scored $\frac{1}{12}$, and Jimmy Perez scored $\frac{1}{8}$ of the Patriots' points. The rest of the Patriots' points were scored by Scottie Jordan.

10a. What fraction of the Patriots' points did Charles, Rigo, and Jimmy score together? Show your work.

Answer _____

10b. What fraction did Scottie score? _____

10c. Rank the players from highest scorer to lowest scorer.

_____   _____   _____   _____
Highest Scorer   *Lowest Scorer*

7. More or Less

1. Compare two fractions that look alike but have different meanings.

1a. The fraction, $\frac{4}{5}$, means divide the whole **unit** into five equal pieces and shade four of them. Shade the following rectangle to show $\frac{4}{5}$.

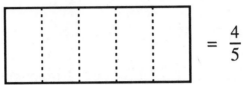

$= \frac{4}{5}$

1b. $\frac{5}{4}$ means divide the whole into four equal pieces and shade five of them. Since the whole unit only has 4 pieces, you cannot shade 5 of them. More than one whole unit is needed. Shade the following rectangles to show $\frac{5}{4}$.

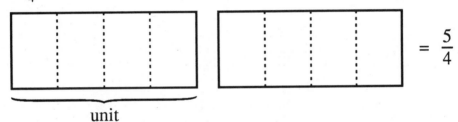

$= \frac{5}{4}$

unit

1c. Which fraction is larger, $\frac{4}{5}$ or $\frac{5}{4}$? _____

The fraction, $\frac{4}{5}$, is a **proper fraction**. The fraction, $\frac{5}{4}$, is an **improper fraction**. The following fractions are proper fractions.

$$\frac{4}{5} \qquad \frac{3}{4} \qquad \frac{3}{5} \qquad \frac{6}{7} \qquad \frac{1}{12} \qquad \frac{7}{25}$$

The following fractions are improper fractions.

$$\frac{5}{4} \qquad \frac{107}{3} \qquad \frac{3}{3} \qquad \frac{13}{7} \qquad \frac{14}{14} \qquad \frac{253}{13} \qquad \frac{73}{73}$$

2. Compare the numerators and the denominators in the proper fractions and then in the improper fractions. What do you notice?

_____

> When the numerator (top) is equal to or larger than the denominator (bottom), the fraction is *improper*. These fractions are larger than or equal to one whole unit.

3a. Is $\frac{529}{530}$ more or less than 1? _____
More or Less

3b. How can you tell just by looking? _____

4a. Is $\frac{531}{530}$ more or less than 1? _____
More or Less

4b. How can you tell just by looking? _____

5a. If a fraction is less than 1, is it proper or improper? _____
Proper or Improper

5b. If a fraction is greater than 1, is it proper or improper? _____
Proper or Improper

5c. If a fraction is equal to 1, is it proper or improper? _____
Proper or Improper

6. In the following problems, write "p" above the proper fractions and "i" above the improper fractions. The first three are done for you.

p	i	i			
$\frac{213}{312}$	$\frac{312}{312}$	$\frac{213}{123}$	$\frac{1}{7}$	$\frac{6}{7}$	$\frac{7}{7}$
$\frac{8}{7}$	$\frac{43}{23}$	$\frac{15}{17}$	$\frac{1,000}{999}$	$\frac{99}{100}$	$\frac{2}{2}$
$\frac{4}{3}$	$\frac{2}{3}$	$\frac{7}{2}$	$\frac{2}{7}$	$\frac{1,000,002}{1,000,000}$	$\frac{999,997}{989,999}$

7a. Will the sum of two improper fractions always be an improper fraction?

Answer _____
Yes or No

7b. Explain and give an example. _____

_____

8a. Will the sum of two proper fractions always be a proper fraction?

Answer _____
Yes or No

8b. Explain and give an example. _____

_____

9. Decide if more or less than 1 whole is shaded. Then write the fraction shown by the pictures and decide if the fraction is proper or improper. The first one is done for you.

	1 Whole	Picture	Fraction
a.		More or (Less)	Number of shaded pieces $\frac{4}{5}$ Number of pieces in 1 whole (Proper) or Improper
b.		More or Less	Proper or Improper
c.		More or Less	Proper or Improper
d.		More or Less	Proper or Improper
e.		More or Less	You shade this fraction. $\frac{19}{12}$ Proper or Improper
f.	You draw.	You draw and shade. More or Less	$\frac{9}{4}$ Proper or Improper

Mixing a Whole Number and a Fraction

1a. What improper fraction is shaded in the following figure?

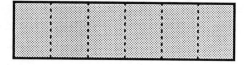 

     Answer _____

1b. Name this shaded improper fraction another way.

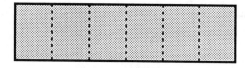 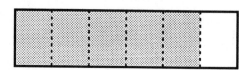

_____ + _____

    How many wholes are shaded?   *Fraction*

A ***mixed number*** is a whole number with a fraction after it. $1 + \frac{5}{6} = 1\frac{5}{6}$. The mixed number, "$1\frac{5}{6}$", is read "one and five-sixths."

2a. Use the following figure to write $\frac{7}{3}$ as a mixed number.

 + + =

_____ + _____ = _____

How many whole   *What fraction of*   *Mixed Number*
circles are shaded?   *a circle is shaded?*

2b. Write the mixed number in words. _____

3a. Is $\frac{9}{7}$ of a rectangle more or less than 1 whole unit? _____

                                                    More or Less

3b. Is $\frac{9}{7}$ of a rectangle more or less than 2 whole units? _____

                                                    More or Less

3c. Shade the following rectangles to show $\frac{9}{7}$. Then change the improper fraction to a mixed number.

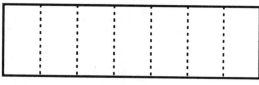 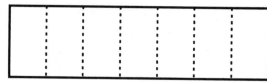

_____ + _____ = _____

 Number of Shaded Wholes   *Fraction*   *Mixed Number*

4a. Shade the following rectangles to show $\frac{15}{9}$.

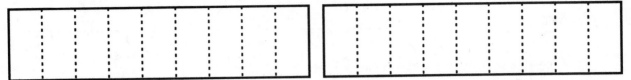

4b. Write $\frac{15}{9}$ as a mixed number in lowest terms. _____

5. Write the improper fraction and mixed number in lowest terms for each shaded picture in the table. The first one is done for you.

	1 Whole	Picture	Improper Fraction	Mixed Number
a.			$\frac{4}{3}$	$1\frac{1}{3}$
b.				
c.				
d.				
e.		*You shade.*	$\frac{7}{5}$	

6a. Is the answer to $\frac{3}{4}$ + $\frac{3}{8}$ closer to $\frac{1}{2}$ or 1? _____

6b. Why? _____

7. Use the following steps to add $\frac{3}{4}$ + $\frac{3}{8}$.

7a. Shade $\frac{3}{4}$ of the first rectangle at the bottom of the page.

 7b. Draw a line(s) in the second rectangle so it is divided into 8 equal pieces. Shade $\frac{3}{8}$ of the second rectangle.

 7c. Cut out the shaded pieces and glue them inside the following rectangles. Fill in as many whole rectangles as possible and do not overlap pieces.

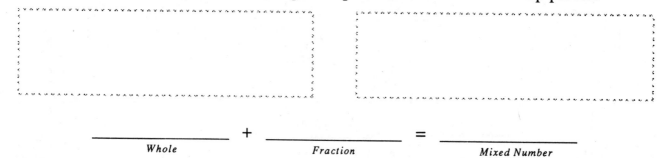

_____ + _____ = _____
        Whole   *Fraction*   *Mixed Number*

 8. Decide whether the answers to the following problems will be a proper fraction or a mixed number. Explain your reasoning for Problems e and f.

a. $\frac{1}{8}$ + $\frac{1}{9}$ + $\frac{1}{10}$ = _____
                                        Proper or Mixed

b. $\frac{1}{8}$ + $\frac{1}{9}$ + $\frac{1}{10}$ + 1 = _____
                                                Proper or Mixed

c. $\frac{7}{12}$ + $\frac{11}{20}$ = _____
                              Proper or Mixed

d. $\frac{3}{8}$ + $\frac{5}{12}$ = _____
                            Proper or Mixed

e. $\frac{5}{4}$ + $\frac{7}{9}$ = _____
                          Proper or Mixed

Explain. _____

f. $\frac{1}{2}$ + $\frac{7}{15}$ = _____
                            Proper or Mixed

Explain. _____

- - - - - - - - - - - - - - - - - - - Cut below this line. - - - - - - - - - - - - - - - -

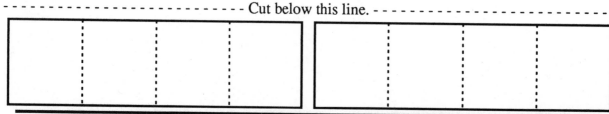

9. Shade the shapes below to help you do the addition problems. Write your answer in lowest terms. Change improper fractions to mixed numbers.

	Problem	Picture	Answer
a.	$\dfrac{3}{4} + \dfrac{3}{4}$		
b.	$\dfrac{4}{5} + \dfrac{9}{10}$		
c.	$\dfrac{5}{12} + \dfrac{5}{6}$		
d.	$\dfrac{5}{12} + \dfrac{1}{3}$		

10. Change the following improper fractions to mixed numbers.

a. $\dfrac{9}{5} = \dfrac{5}{5} + \dfrac{\boxed{}}{5} =$ _____
Mixed Number

b. $\dfrac{11}{5} = \dfrac{5}{5} + \dfrac{5}{5} + \dfrac{\boxed{}}{5} =$ _____
Mixed Number

c. $\dfrac{21}{5} =$ _____
Mixed Number

d. $\dfrac{43}{5} =$ _____
Mixed Number

11a. To change $\frac{1,234}{15}$ to a mixed number, find how many whole fifteens are in 1,234 using trial and error. Complete the following table.

| Guess
How many whole fifteens are in 1,234? | Answer
How close to 1,234 can you get? |
| --- | --- |
| 10 | $15 \times 10 = 150$
Too small. |
| 50 | $15 \times 50 = 750$
Too small. |
| What is your next try? | Too big or too small? |
| What is your next try? | Too big or too small? |
| What is your next try? | Too big or too small? |
| What is your next try? | Too big or too small? |
| What is your next try? | Too big or too small? |
| What is your next try? | Too big or too small? |
| What is your next try? | Too big or too small? |
| What is your next try? | Too big or too small? |
| What is your next try? | Too big or too small? |

11b. How many whole fifteens are in 1,234? _____

11c. You did not get 1,234 exactly. What number did you get? _____

11d. How far away are you from 1,234? _____

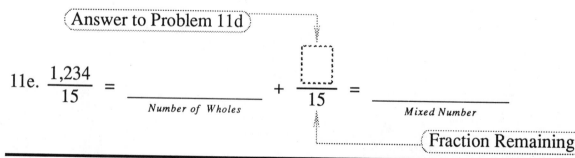

11e. $\dfrac{1,234}{15}$ = _____ + $\dfrac{\boxed{}}{15}$ = _____

Number of Wholes ⟶ ⟵ *Mixed Number*

Fraction Remaining

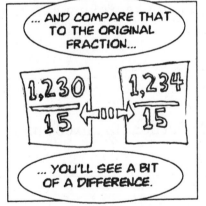

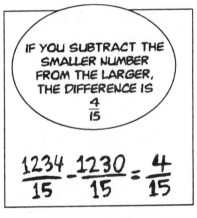

12. Use the following steps to change $\frac{1,597}{17}$ to a mixed number.

12a. List keystrokes to find the number of wholes in $\frac{1,597}{17}$.

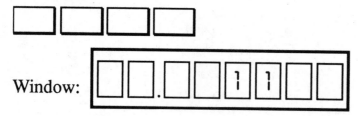

Window:

12b. Circle the part of the window that shows the number of wholes.

12c. Multiply the number of wholes by 17. Write your answer in the following figure.

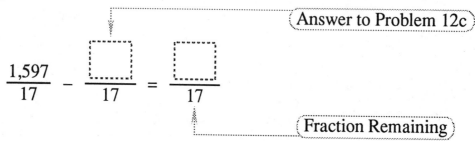

12d. Subtract to find the fraction remaining. Write your answer in the figure above.

12e. $\frac{1,597}{17}$ = _____ + _____ = _____
     Number of Wholes   *Fraction Remaining*   *Mixed Number*

13. Change the improper fractions to mixed numbers in lowest terms.

13a. $\frac{123}{5}$ = _____ + _____ = _____
     Number of Wholes   *Fraction Remaining*   *Mixed Number*

13b. $\frac{566}{8}$ = _____ + _____ = _____
     Number of Wholes   *Fraction Remaining*   *Mixed Number*

13c. $\frac{2,654}{13}$ = _____ + _____ = _____
     Number of Wholes   *Fraction Remaining*   *Mixed Number*

13d. $\frac{794}{17}$ = _____ + _____ = _____
     Number of Wholes   *Fraction Remaining*   *Mixed Number*

13e. $\frac{5,697}{26}$ = _____ + _____ = _____
     Number of Wholes   *Fraction Remaining*   *Mixed Number*

14. Change the improper fractions to mixed numbers in lowest terms.

    a. $\frac{76}{25}$ = _____   b. $\frac{53}{3}$ = _____

    c. $\frac{1,000}{11}$ = _____   d. $\frac{1,000}{22}$ = _____

    e. $\frac{1,234}{4}$ = _____   f. $\frac{1,236}{4}$ = _____

    g. $\frac{565}{15}$ = _____   h. $\frac{2,566}{15}$ = _____

Calling It by a Different Name

1. The junior high class ordered five pizzas and ate $2\frac{2}{3}$ pizzas.
   The remaining pizza was saved for the office staff. A problem like
   $5 - 2\frac{2}{3}$ looks easy, but it can be tricky.

1a. In the following figure, cross out $2\frac{2}{3}$ pizzas. Then count to find how
   much pizza remains.

        ◯   ◯   ◯   ◯   ◯

$5 - 2\frac{2}{3}$ = _____

1b. To subtract $2\frac{2}{3}$ from 5, you must do some name changing.

The five wholes will become a mixed number, $4 + \frac{3}{3}$, as shown below.

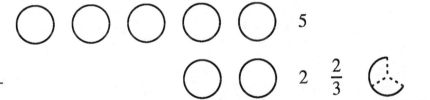

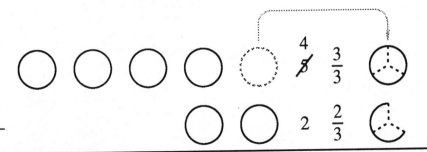

Why is 5 changed to $4\frac{3}{3}$ instead of mixed numbers like $4\frac{6}{6}$, $4\frac{5}{5}$, or $4\frac{2}{2}$?

_____

1c. $4\frac{3}{3} - 2\frac{2}{3} =$ _____

Compare with Problem 1a.

1d. Gerald wrote the problem $5 - 2\frac{2}{3} = 3\frac{2}{3}$. Explain to Gerald why his answer is too large.

_____

 2a. Draw a picture to solve the problem $7 - 4\frac{2}{5}$.

2b. Now solve $7 - 4\frac{2}{5}$ by changing the 7 into a mixed number.

$$7 - 4\frac{2}{5} = 6\frac{\boxed{}}{\boxed{}} - 4\frac{2}{5}$$

Answer _____

Compare with Problem 2a.

3. Find $8 - 2\frac{3}{7}$. Remember to change the 8 into a mixed number.

$8 - 2\frac{3}{7} =$ _____

The answer is not $6\frac{3}{7}$.

 4. Solve the following problems. Be careful! Change whole numbers into mixed numbers when necessary.

a. $5 - 3\frac{1}{2} =$ _____   b. $5\frac{1}{2} - 3 =$ _____

c. $6\frac{4}{11} - 4 =$ _____   d. $6 - 4\frac{4}{11} =$ _____

e. $10 - 9\frac{3}{5} =$ _____   f. $10\frac{3}{5} - 9 =$ _____

g. $1 - \frac{1}{10} - \frac{1}{10} - \frac{1}{10} - \frac{1}{10} - \frac{1}{10} - \frac{1}{10} - \frac{1}{10} =$ _____

5. To solve the problem $3\frac{2}{7} - 1\frac{6}{7}$,
   $3\frac{2}{7}$ must be changed into a
   different mixed number.

5a. Why? _____

   _____

   _____

5b. $3\frac{2}{7} - 1\frac{6}{7} = $ _____

$$3\frac{2}{7} = \boxed{3} + \frac{2}{7}$$

$$3\frac{2}{7} = 2\frac{7}{7} + \frac{2}{7}$$

$$3\frac{2}{7} = 2\frac{9}{7}$$

Change to a mixed number.

6. Use the steps at the right to solve $9\frac{1}{6} - 2\frac{5}{6}$.
   Parentheses, ( ), are used to change
   $9\frac{1}{6}$ into a different mixed number.

$$9\frac{1}{6} - 2\frac{5}{6}$$

$$(9 + \frac{1}{6}) - 2\frac{5}{6}$$

$$(8\,\frac{\boxed{}}{\boxed{}} + \frac{1}{6}) - 2\frac{5}{6}$$

$$(8\,\frac{\boxed{}}{6}) - 2\frac{5}{6}$$

Answer _____

7. Solve $7\frac{3}{11} - 5\frac{10}{11}$. The steps are
   started for you at the right.

$$7\frac{3}{11} - 5\frac{10}{11}$$

$$(7 + \frac{\boxed{}}{11}) - 5\frac{10}{11}$$

$$(6\,\frac{\boxed{}}{\boxed{}} + \frac{\boxed{}}{11}) - 5\frac{10}{11}$$

Answer _____

8. Do the following subtraction problems. Show your work.

   a. $10 - \frac{1}{2} - \frac{1}{2} - \frac{1}{2} - \frac{1}{2} - \frac{1}{2} =$ _____

   b. $5\frac{3}{7} - \frac{1}{7} - \frac{1}{7} - \frac{1}{7} - \frac{1}{7} - \frac{1}{7} =$ _____

   c. $15\frac{3}{17} - 2\frac{10}{17} =$ _____

   d. $9\frac{8}{15} - 4\frac{11}{15} =$ _____

9. Find $8\frac{1}{2} - 6\frac{4}{5}$ using the following steps.

9a. Write $8\frac{1}{2} - 6\frac{4}{5}$ as a problem with a common denominator.

9b. Subtract by "borrowing" from the 8.

   Answer _____

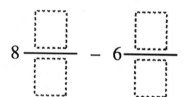

10. Find $3\frac{1}{3} - 2\frac{3}{4}$ using the following steps.

10a. Rewrite $3\frac{1}{3} - 2\frac{3}{4}$ using a common denominator.

10b. "Borrow" and subtract.

   Answer _____

   The answer is less than 1.

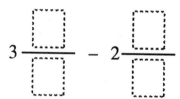

11. Subtract the following. Reduce your answers to lowest terms. Show your work.

   a. $7\frac{1}{2} - 2\frac{3}{4} =$ _____   b. $22\frac{3}{7} - 4\frac{3}{4} =$ _____

   c. $9\frac{2}{7} - 4\frac{5}{6} =$ _____   d. $11\frac{3}{8} - 7\frac{7}{9} =$ _____

Homework 7: More or Less

 1. Do the following problems in your head.

a. $\dfrac{1}{7} + \dfrac{4}{7} + \dfrac{\boxed{}}{7} = 1$

b. $\dfrac{1}{4} + \dfrac{1}{4} + \dfrac{\boxed{}}{\boxed{}} = 1$

c. $\dfrac{1}{2} + \dfrac{1}{2} + \dfrac{1}{2} + \dfrac{1}{2} + \dfrac{1}{2} = $ _____

d. $\dfrac{2}{5} + \dfrac{\boxed{}}{\boxed{}} = 1\dfrac{1}{5}$

e. $\dfrac{7}{10} + \dfrac{\boxed{}}{\boxed{}} + \dfrac{9}{10} = 2\dfrac{1}{10}$

f. $\dfrac{1}{2} + \dfrac{\boxed{}}{\boxed{}} = \dfrac{3}{4}$

g. $\dfrac{3}{10} + \dfrac{\boxed{}}{10} = \dfrac{1}{6} + \dfrac{1}{6} + \dfrac{1}{6} + \dfrac{1}{6} + \dfrac{1}{6} + \dfrac{1}{6}$

h. $\dfrac{1}{2} + \dfrac{1}{4} + \dfrac{1}{4} + \dfrac{1}{2} + \dfrac{2}{3} + \dfrac{1}{3} + \dfrac{1}{2} = $ _____

j. $\dfrac{3}{4} + \dfrac{1}{2} + \dfrac{1}{2} + \dfrac{1}{3} + \dfrac{1}{4} + \dfrac{1}{3} = $ _____

k. $\dfrac{1}{2} + \dfrac{1}{2} + \dfrac{\boxed{}}{\boxed{}} = 1\dfrac{4}{7}$

m. $\dfrac{\boxed{}}{\boxed{}} + 1\dfrac{1}{2} + 1\dfrac{1}{2} + 1\dfrac{1}{2} = 5$

2. Maneuverville Junior High is planning their annual school play. Marilynne, a seamstress, needs $1\frac{1}{3}$ yards of velvet for the prince's tunic and $3\frac{3}{4}$ yards of velvet for the queen's cape. How many yards of velvet does Marilynne need to buy?

Answer _____ yards

3. Each member of the cast plays one role in the school play. $\frac{2}{5}$ of the cast plays pirates and $\frac{1}{3}$ of the cast plays heroes. What fraction of the cast plays roles other than pirates or heroes?

Answer _____

4. The treasurer of the theater club reported the following:

   $\frac{3}{16}$ of their money is allotted for costumes

   $\frac{1}{4}$ is allotted for the stage crew

   $\frac{1}{8}$ is allotted for the prop crew

   $\frac{1}{8}$ is allotted for lighting and sound

The remaining money is allotted for promotion. What fraction is left for the promotion of the play?

Answer _____

5. Juanita made a sign for the entrance of the theater. She made a $\frac{3}{4}$ inch mark and then a $\frac{1}{2}$ inch mark. She made another $\frac{3}{4}$ inch mark followed by a $\frac{1}{2}$ inch mark. She followed this pattern 18 more times. How long was the sign? The problem is started for you.

$$\left(\frac{3}{4} + \frac{1}{2}\right) + \left(\frac{3}{4} + \frac{1}{2}\right) + \left(\frac{3}{4} + \frac{1}{2}\right)\ldots$$

Length of sign _____ inches

8. The "Prime" Building Blocks

The number 15 can be built by multiplying smaller numbers. For example, 15 = 3 × 5. A number that can be built by multiplying smaller whole numbers is called a *composite number*. The numbers, 24, 35, 100, and 51, are composite numbers.

$$24 = 8 \times 3$$
$$35 = 5 \times 7$$
$$100 = 10 \times 10$$
$$51 = 3 \times 17$$

The number 17 cannot be built by multiplying smaller whole numbers. It is called a *prime number*. (17 is 17 × 1, but you can always multiply by 1.)

Here is a list of the first seven prime numbers. (Notice "1" is not on the list.)

2, 3, 5, 7, 11, 13, 17

 1a. Find the next five prime numbers. If the number is **composite**, write it as a multiplication problem. If the number is **prime**, write "prime." The first one is done for you. Stop when you find 5 primes.

18 = 6 x 3   29 = _____

19 = _____   30 = _____

20 = _____   31 = _____

21 = _____   32 = _____

22 = _____   33 = _____

23 = _____   34 = _____

24 = _____   35 = _____

25 = _____   36 = _____

26 = _____   37 = _____

27 = _____   38 = _____

28 = _____   39 = _____

1b. List the next five prime numbers.

2, 3, 5, 7, 11, 13, 17, _____, _____, _____, _____, _____

Maneuvers with Fractions

2. A *prime number* is a number that has exactly two different factors, 1 and itself. A neat method to find prime numbers is to use the Sieve of Eratosthenes (air-uh-tos-thin-ease). Eratosthenes was a Greek mathematician. Use the list of counting numbers below and the following steps to find the prime numbers between 1 and 130.

   a. The number 1 is a special number. It has only one factor, so it is not prime. Cross out the number 1.

   b. Using a colored pen, circle 2 to show that it is a prime number.

   c. Cross out all of the numbers that are evenly divisible by 2. Since 2 is a factor of these numbers, we know they cannot be prime. Notice the pattern: skip, cross out, skip, cross out, skip, . . .

   d. Go back to the smallest number that is not crossed out. It is 3. Using a colored pen, circle 3 to show that it is prime.

   e. Cross out all of the numbers that are evenly divisible by 3. If a number is already crossed out, cross it out again. Find the pattern.

   f. Go back to the smallest number that is not crossed out or circled. Circle it because it is prime. Cross out all of the numbers that are evenly divisible by this prime number.

   g. Repeat Step **f** until you find all the prime numbers less than 130.

1	2	3	4	5	6	7	8	9	10
11	12	13	14	15	16	17	18	19	20
21	22	23	24	25	26	27	28	29	30
31	32	33	34	35	36	37	38	39	40
41	42	43	44	45	46	47	48	49	50
51	52	53	54	55	56	57	58	59	60
61	62	63	64	65	66	67	68	69	70
71	72	73	74	75	76	77	78	79	80
81	82	83	84	85	86	87	88	89	90
91	92	93	94	95	96	97	98	99	100
101	102	103	104	105	106	107	108	109	110
111	112	113	114	115	116	117	118	119	120
121	122	123	124	125	126	127	128	129	130

In a book about prime numbers, it states that 2,305,843,009,213,693,951 is a prime number. To check this, you would need a computer and time.

3. Instead of the monstrous number above, check a smaller number. Is 131 a prime number? In this problem, use the first 6 primes (2, 3, 5, 7, 11, and 13) to decide if 131 is a prime number.

3a. Press: | 131 | STO |

    Every time you need | 131 |, press | RCL |. Do not press | AC/ON |.

3b. Press: | RCL | ÷ | 2 | = | Is 131 divisible by 2? _____
                                                                                                   Yes or No

3c. Press: | RCL | ÷ | 3 | = | Is 131 divisible by 3? _____
    Yes or No

3d. Press: | RCL | ÷ | 5 | = | Is 131 divisible by 5? _____
    Yes or No

3e. Press: | RCL | ÷ | 7 | = | Is 131 divisible by 7? _____
    Yes or No

3f. Press: | RCL | ÷ | 11 | = | Is 131 divisible by 11? _____
    Yes or No

3g. Press: | RCL | ÷ | 13 | = | Is 131 divisible by 13? _____
    Yes or No

3h. If you answered "yes" to any of the questions above, 131 is composite. If you answered "no" to every question above, 131 is prime.

    Is 131 prime or composite? _____
                                        Prime or Composite

4. Decide if 141 is a prime number.

4a. Press: | 141 | STO |

4b. Press: | RCL | ÷ | 2 | = | Is 141 divisible by 2? _____
    Yes or No

4c. Press: | RCL | ÷ | 3 | = | Is 141 divisible by 3? _____
    Yes or No

4d. Is 141 prime or composite? _____
                                  Prime or Composite

5. Is 1,259 a prime number? Use the first 13 primes to decide.

5a. Press: | 1259 | | STO |

5b. Every time you need | 1259 |, press | RCL |. Do not press | AC/ON |. Round each answer to the nearest tenth and write it on the answer line. If dividing by a prime number gives a whole number, you can stop.

RCL	÷	2	=	_____
RCL	÷	3	=	_____
RCL	÷	5	=	_____
RCL	÷	7	=	_____
RCL	÷	11	=	_____
RCL	÷	13	=	_____
RCL	÷	17	=	_____
RCL	÷	19	=	_____
RCL	÷	23	=	_____
RCL	÷	29	=	_____
RCL	÷	31	=	_____
RCL	÷	37	=	_____
RCL	÷	41	=	_____

5c. Is 1,259 a prime number? _____
                           Yes or No

5d. Look at the order of the prime numbers. Now look at the order of the calculated answers. Why do you think the steps could stop at "37?"

As you experiment to find factors, you only need to use prime numbers. For reference, here is a list of prime numbers up to 200.

2, 3, 5, 7, 11, 13, 17, 19, 23, 29, 31, 37, 41, 43, 47, 53, 59, 61, 67, 71, 73, 79, 83, 89, 97, 101, 103, 107, 109, 113, 127, 131, 137, 139, 149, 151, 157, 163, 167, 173, 179, 181, 191, 193, 197, 199

6. Why couldn't 2,865,307,748 be a prime number?

_____

7. Why couldn't 2,865,307,745 be a prime number?

_____

8. Why couldn't 2,865,307,740 be a prime number?

_____

 9. Three of the following numbers are composite. Write the composite numbers as a product of two factors. Write "P" next to the prime number.

135,792 = _____   56,389 = _____

2,131 = _____   51,051 = _____

Prime Factorization

When a number is written as a multiplication problem with prime number factors, it is called a ***prime factorization***. A prime factorization usually lists the factors from smallest to largest.

18 = 2 × (9) ⟵ —————————————— Not a prime factor

18 = (2) × (3) × (3) ——————— Prime factorization

50 = 5 × (10) ⟵ ————————— Not a prime factor

50 = (2) × (5) × (5) ——————— Prime factorization

24 = 3 × (8) ⟵ ————————— Not a prime factor

24 = (____ × ____ × ____ × ____) ⟵ Write the prime factorization of 24. Write the factors from smallest to largest.

————————— Not prime factors

100 = (10) × (10)

100 = (____ × ____ × ____ × ____) ⟵ Write the prime factorization of 100.

Use mental arithmetic to write these numbers as a product of prime factors.
Write the factors from smallest to largest.

1a. 15 = _____   1b. 30 = _____

2a. 32 = _____   2b. 96 = _____

3a. 42 = _____   3b. 126 = _____

4a. 210 = _____   4b. 420 = _____

5a. 1,000 = _____

5b. 6,000 = _____

6a. 10,000 = _____

6b. 20,000 = _____

7. Find the prime factorization of 76,440 using the following steps.

7a. Complete the table. The first steps are done for you.

Number to be Factored	Prime Factor	Other Factor
76,440	2	76,440 ÷ 2 = 38,220
38,220	2	38,220 ÷ 2 = 19,110
19,110	2	19,110 ÷ 2 = 9,555
9,555 *2 does not work!* *Why not?*	*Next highest prime* 3	9,555 ÷ 3 = 3,185
3,185 *3 does not work!*	*Next highest prime* 5	3,185 ÷ 5 = 637
637 *5 does not work!* *Why not?*	*Next highest prime* 7	

7b. Write the prime factorization of 76,440.

Answer _____

8a. Write 1,646,008 as a product of prime factors using the following table.

Number to be Factored	Prime Factor	Another Factor
1,646,008	2	1,646,008 ÷ 2 =
	2	
19	19	19 ÷ 19 = 1

8b. Write the prime factorization of 1,646,008.

Answer _____

9a. Write 2,674,763 as a product of prime factors using the following table.

Number to be Factored	Prime Factor	Another Factor
2,674,763 *2, 3, and 5 do not work!*	7	2,674,763 ÷ 7 = 382,109

9b. Write the prime factorization of 2,674,763. _____

Canceling

Fractions can be reduced "easily" by finding the prime factorization of the numerator and denominator. For example, the fraction $\frac{168}{252}$ is rewritten using the prime factorizations.

$$\frac{168}{252} = \frac{2 \times 2 \times 2 \times 3 \times 7}{2 \times 2 \times 3 \times 3 \times 7}$$

1a. If we divide the numerator and denominator by the same number, we get an equal fraction. Cross out the common factors that are on the top and the bottom. Most people call this *canceling*.

1b. The new fraction is: $\dfrac{\boxed{}}{\boxed{}}$

1c. Is the new fraction equal to $\frac{168}{252}$? _____
    Yes or No

1d. How did you check? _____

_____

If all the common factors are canceled, the fraction is guaranteed to be in lowest terms.

2a. Write the prime factorization of the numerator and the denominator.

$$\frac{66}{455} = \text{_____}$$

2b. Cancel common factors.

2c. Write your result as a fraction in lowest terms. $\dfrac{\boxed{}}{\boxed{}}$

3. What can you say about $\frac{66}{455}$? _____

_____

To find the lowest terms of a complicated fraction, write the numerator and denominator as a product of prime number factors. Then divide (cancel out) all equal factors in the numerator and the denominator.

Write the prime factorization of both the numerator and denominator. Divide (cancel out) as many common factors as possible. Write your result as a fraction in lowest terms.

4. $\dfrac{24}{36}$ = ——————————— = $\dfrac{\boxed{}}{\boxed{}}$

5. $\dfrac{80}{205}$ = ——————————— = $\dfrac{\boxed{}}{\boxed{}}$

6. $\dfrac{369}{963}$ = ——————————— = $\dfrac{\boxed{}}{\boxed{}}$

7. $\dfrac{70{,}785}{99{,}099}$ = ——————————— = $\dfrac{\boxed{}}{\boxed{}}$

8. $\dfrac{1{,}592{,}656}{1{,}489{,}904}$ = ——————————— = $\dfrac{\boxed{}}{\boxed{}}$ = —————————
Mixed Number

9. To find the prime factorization of 2,500, you can divide by 10 and then divide by 10 again. But 10 is not a prime number. So each time you divide by 10, write down 2 and 5 as factors.

$\dfrac{2{,}500}{22{,}500}$ = ——————————— = $\dfrac{\boxed{}}{\boxed{}}$ Not "0"

Prime Numbers Never Quit

Prime numbers thin out as numbers get bigger. For example, between 1 and 1,000 there are 168 primes. In the thousand numbers between 1,000,000 and 1,001,000, there are 75 primes. Around the year 300 B.C., the Greek mathematician, Euclid, proved that prime numbers go on forever. Although there are fewer primes as the numbers get bigger, primes never stop.

1. The prime numbers 2 and 3 are the only two primes that are side by side. After 2, there are no other even prime numbers. Why are all other even numbers composite?

   _____

   _____

Sometimes there are two odd prime numbers that are only two apart.

For example: 11 and 13; 17 and 19; 191 and 193

These pairs are called *twin primes*.

2. Find a pair of twin primes between 17, 19 and 191, 193. _____

3. Tracy's answer was 51 and 53. What is wrong with Tracy's answer?

   _____

There are fewer primes as the numbers get bigger. Do twin primes go on forever or do they quit? Nobody knows for sure. Big hunts with the fastest computers have given hints that twin primes go on forever. But until a mathematician figures out a way to prove it, we will not know for sure.

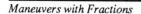

Homework 8: The "Prime" Building Blocks

1. Christopher wrote the prime factorization for 7,487,480 but forgot to record one of the factors.

   $7{,}487{,}480 = 2 \times 2 \times 2 \times 7 \times 11 \times 11 \times 13 \times 17$

   What factor did he forget? _____

2a. Jasmine was supposed to give the prime factorization of 4,288,284. She correctly factored as follows:

   $4{,}288{,}284 = 2 \times 2 \times 7 \times 7 \times 9 \times 11 \times 13 \times 17$

   Why isn't this a complete **prime** factorization? _____

   _____

2b. Write the prime factorization of 4,288,284.

   $4{,}288{,}284 =$ _____

3. In the problems below, you are given a correct factorization.
   Factor the non-primes until you get a prime factorization.
   List the prime factorization from smallest to largest under each problem.

   It would be smart to multiply the prime factorization on the calculator to be sure you are right.

   a. $248{,}832 = 6 \times 2 \times 12 \times 12 \times 12 \times 12$

   b. $1{,}125{,}579 = 7 \times 13 \times 19 \times 21 \times 31$

4. Use the following steps to find the prime factorization of 137,899,720. The calculator will not accept this number into its window.

4a. What number is a factor of 137,899,720?

   Answer _____

4b. Divide 137,899,720 by the answer to Problem 4a. _____

4c. Write the prime factorization of 137,899,720.

   $137{,}899{,}720 =$ _____

5a. What year were you born? _____

5b. Is this number prime or composite? _____

Prime or Composite

5c. How did you decide? _____

 6a. Calculate: $2 \times 3 \times 5 \times 7 \times 11 \times 13 \oplus 1 =$ _____

6b. Is your answer a prime number? _____ $\widehat{\text{Be careful!}}$

Yes or No

6c. If it is composite, list two of its factors. _____ and _____

7. After Donna finished canceling common prime factors, her fraction looked like $\frac{3 \times 13}{5 \times 19}$. Donna canceled a 2, 3, and 11.

What was the original fraction Donna reduced? _____

 8. Compare each pair of fractions. Decide if the first fraction is greater than, less than, or equal to the second fraction.

a. $\dfrac{5 \times 11 \times 11}{5 \times 11 \times 11}$ _____ $\dfrac{1}{2}$

Greater, Less, or Equal

b. $\dfrac{2 \times 2 \times 2 \times 3 \times 3 \times 5}{2 \times 2 \times 3 \times 3 \times 5}$ _____ $\dfrac{2 \times 2 \times 2 \times 2 \times 3 \times 5 \times 7}{2 \times 2 \times 2 \times 2 \times 5 \times 7}$

Greater, Less, or Equal

c. $\dfrac{5 \times 7 \times 11 \times 11 \times 13}{5 \times 5 \times 7 \times 11 \times 11 \times 13}$ _____ $\dfrac{2 \times 3 \times 7 \times 7 \times 7}{2 \times 2 \times 3 \times 3 \times 7 \times 7 \times 7}$

Greater, Less, or Equal

9. Four numbers have each been written as a prime factorization. Decide whether the fractions make a proportion. Write "Yes" or "No."

a. $\dfrac{2 \times 2 \times 3 \times 5}{2 \times 2 \times 2 \times 17} \overset{?}{=} \dfrac{2 \times 3 \times 5 \times 5}{2 \times 2 \times 5 \times 17}$ _____

Yes or No

b. $\dfrac{2 \times 7 \times 7 \times 11}{2 \times 3 \times 7 \times 11 \times 13} \overset{?}{=} \dfrac{2 \times 3 \times 3 \times 5 \times 7 \times 11}{2 \times 3 \times 3 \times 3 \times 5 \times 7 \times 11 \times 13}$ _____

Yes or No

10a. If you add two prime numbers, will the sum ever be a prime number?

Answer _____

Yes or No

10b. If you answered "yes," give an example. _____

10c. If you answered "no," explain why not. _____

_____

9. Traveling Through Time

1a. Johnny and Erin each had 18 crickets. Johnny put $\frac{1}{2}$ of his crickets in a jar. Put a loop around $\frac{1}{2}$ of the crickets in the following picture.

1b. $\frac{1}{2}$ of 18 crickets = _____ crickets

2a. Erin put $\frac{1}{3}$ of her crickets in an aquarium. Put a loop around $\frac{1}{3}$ of the crickets in the following picture.

2b. $\frac{1}{3}$ of 18 crickets = _____ crickets

3. $\frac{2}{3}$ of Erin's crickets are not in the aquarium. How many crickets are not in the aquarium?

$\frac{2}{3}$ of 18 crickets = _____ crickets

4a. A flock of 45 birds is flying south. $\frac{2}{5}$ of the birds decide to fly to Hawaii. Divide the flock into fifths with loops.

4b. $\frac{1}{5}$ of 45 = _____

4c. $\frac{2}{5}$ of 45 = _____

$\frac{2}{5}$ of 45 is the same as $\frac{2}{5} \times 45$.

4d. $\frac{2}{5} \times 45 =$ _____

5a. Jenny has 12 oranges. She wants to use $\frac{1}{2}$ of the oranges in a fruit salad. How many oranges should Jenny use?

Answer _____ oranges

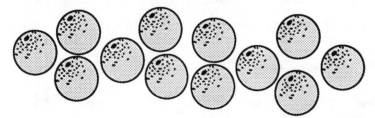

$\frac{1}{2}$ of 12 = 6

$\frac{1}{2}$ × 12 = 6

5b. Jenny looked at her problem another way. Instead of $\frac{1}{2}$ × 12, she turned it around and multiplied 12 × $\frac{1}{2}$. "I can use 12 one-half pieces."

$$12 \times \frac{1}{2} = \left(\frac{1}{2} + \frac{1}{2}\right) + \left(\frac{1}{2} + \frac{1}{2}\right) + \left(\frac{1}{2} + \frac{1}{2}\right) + \left(\frac{1}{2} + \frac{1}{2}\right) + \left(\frac{1}{2} + \frac{1}{2}\right) + \left(\frac{1}{2} + \frac{1}{2}\right)$$

     1   1   1   1   1   1

$12 \times \frac{1}{2}$ = _____

Multiplication always gives the same answer in either order.

$$12 \times \frac{1}{2} = \frac{1}{2} \times 12$$

If you have a multiplication problem and don't like the order, reverse it.

---

6. Solve the following problems in your head.

a. $\frac{1}{3}$ × 6 = _____   b. $\frac{2}{3}$ × 6 = _____

c. 24 × $\frac{1}{4}$ = _____   d. 24 × $\frac{3}{4}$ = _____

e. $\frac{1}{5}$ × 100 = _____   f. $\frac{3}{5}$ × 100 = _____

g. $\frac{4}{4}$ × 8 = _____   h. $\frac{4}{4}$ × 1,212 = _____

j. 21 × $\frac{2}{7}$ = _____   k. 21 × $\frac{5}{7}$ = _____

Fractions of Time

1. Latoya has 1 hour (60 minutes) to get to the bus stop. The clock face at the right shows 60 minutes.

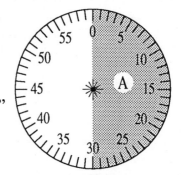

1a. She spent the first $\frac{1}{2}$ hour getting ready for school.

$\frac{1}{2}$ hour is shaded on the clock face and is labeled "A."

How many minutes are in $\frac{1}{2}$ hour?

Answer _____ minutes

1b. Latoya spent her next $\frac{1}{4}$ hour eating breakfast. Shade $\frac{1}{4}$ hour and label it "B."

How many minutes are in $\frac{1}{4}$ hour? _____ minutes

1c. After breakfast, it took her 10 minutes to make her lunch. Shade 10 minutes on the clock and label it "C."

What fraction of an hour is 10 minutes? _____ hour

1d. It took her $\frac{1}{12}$ hour to walk to the bus stop. Shade $\frac{1}{12}$ hour and label it "D."

How many minutes are in $\frac{1}{12}$ hour? _____ minutes

1e. Was Latoyta on time for the bus? _____
    Yes or No

2. Latoya's brother, Shafer, overslept, so he only has $\frac{1}{2}$ hour to get to the bus stop. In order to catch the bus, he has to spend $\frac{1}{2}$ of the time that Latoya spent on each activity. Use Latoya's clock to help you shade and label the clock below. Then complete the table.

Activity	Half of Latoya's Time	Fraction of the Hour	Number of Minutes
Getting Ready	$\frac{1}{2}$ of $\frac{1}{2}$ =	$\frac{1}{4}$	
Breakfast	$\frac{1}{2}$ of $\frac{1}{4}$ =		7.5
Making Lunch	$\frac{1}{2}$ of $\frac{1}{6}$ =		
Running to the Bus Stop	$\frac{1}{2}$ of $\frac{1}{12}$ =		

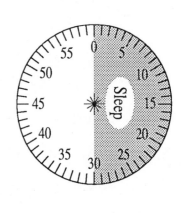

3. Record your morning activities for 1 hour before school. Shade the clock face and label each section. Then complete the table.

Activity	Number of Minutes	Fraction of the Hour

4. Julio told Latoya that it took him $\frac{2}{3}$ of the $\frac{1}{2}$ hour it took her to get ready for school.

4a. Divide the shaded $\frac{1}{2}$ hour into thirds.

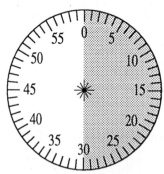

4b. Shade $\frac{2}{3}$ of the $\frac{1}{2}$ hour.

4c. How many minutes did it take Julio to get ready for school?

Answer _____ minutes

4d. What fraction of an hour is this? _____ hour

4e. **Without the clock, Julio noticed that when he multiplied the numerators and the denominators, he got the same answer. First, he canceled the 2's because** $\frac{2}{2} = 1$.

$$\frac{2}{3} \times \frac{1}{2} = \frac{2 \times 1}{3 \times 2} = \frac{1}{3} \text{ hour}$$

Does Julio's answer match Problem 4c? _____
Yes or No

Explain. _____

> To multiply fractions, multiply the numerators to get a new numerator and multiply the denominators to get a new denominator. Cancel common factors before you multiply.

5. Deidre said, "I got ready for school in $\frac{9}{10}$ of Julio's time." She wrote the following problem. Notice that she canceled a pair of 2's.

$$\frac{9}{10} \times \frac{2}{3} \times \frac{1}{2} = \frac{\overset{3}{9} \times 2 \times 1}{10 \times 3 \times 2} = \frac{\Box}{\Box} \text{ hour}$$

5a. What else did she cancel? _____

5b. What fraction of an hour did it take Deidre to get ready for school? Write your answer in the boxes.

5c. How many minutes is that? _____ minutes

6. Do the following problems. Cancel when possible.

a. $\frac{2}{3} \times \frac{3}{4} =$ _____ hour   How many minutes? _____

b. $\frac{3}{4} \times \frac{2}{3} =$ _____ hour   How many minutes? _____

c. $\frac{2}{5} \times \frac{1}{2} =$ _____ hour   How many minutes? _____

d. $\frac{4}{5} \times \frac{3}{4} =$ _____ hour   How many minutes? _____

7. Before multiplying the following problems, reduce or cancel.

a. $\frac{1}{2} \times \frac{3}{5} =$ _____

b. $\frac{3}{3} \times \frac{3}{4} =$ _____

c. $\frac{4}{15} \times \frac{6}{15} =$ _____

d. $\frac{9}{15} \times \frac{15}{24} =$ _____

e. $\frac{21}{64} \times \frac{8}{9} =$ _____

f. $\frac{2}{3} \times \frac{3}{4} \times \frac{4}{5} \times \frac{5}{6} =$ _____

g. $\frac{100}{100} \times \frac{600}{800} =$ _____

h. $\frac{1}{10} \times \frac{1}{10} \times \frac{1}{10} \times \frac{1,000}{1,001} =$ _____

8a. Which two answers in Problem 7 are the same? _____ and _____

8b. Which answer in Problem 7 is the smallest? _____

8c. What three answers total one whole? _____ + _____ + _____

Larger and Smaller

If the numerator and the denominator of a fraction are equal, the fraction is equal to 1. Since $\frac{16}{16} = 1$, then $\frac{16}{16} \times 187$ is equal to $1 \times 187 = 187$.

If the numerator is twice the denominator, the fraction is equal to 2. Since $\frac{32}{16} = 2$, then $\frac{32}{16} \times 187$ is equal to $2 \times 187 = 374$.

1a. Since 187 is less than 200, then $\frac{32}{16} \times 187$ is less than _____.

1b. Since 287 is less than 300, then $\frac{32}{16} \times 287$ is less than _____.

1c. Since 496 is less then 500, then $\frac{48}{16} \times 496$ is less than _____.

Hint: What does $\frac{48}{16}$ equal?

Circle the best answer without using your calculator.

2a. $\frac{10}{5}$ is closest to

1   2   5   50

2b. $\frac{10.1}{5}$ is closest to

1   2   5   50

2c. $\frac{10.1}{5} \times 100$ is closest to

100   200   500   510

3a. $\frac{30}{10}$ is closest to

$\frac{1}{3}$ 1   2   3

3b. $\frac{30}{9.8}$ is closest to

$\frac{1}{3}$ 1   2   3

3c. $\frac{30}{9.8} \times 1,000$ is closest to

300   1,000   2,000   3,000

4a. $\frac{45}{15}$ is closest to

$\frac{1}{3}$ 2   3   60

4b. $\frac{46}{15}$ is closest to

$\frac{1}{3}$ 2   3   61

4c. $\frac{46}{15} \times 200$ is closest to

100   200   600   1,200

5a. $\frac{10}{20}$ is closest to

0.3 $\frac{1}{2}$ 1.2   30

5b. $\frac{10.037}{20.129} \times 100$ is closest to

30   50   120   300

6a. $\frac{40}{10}$ is closest to

$\frac{1}{4}$ $\frac{1}{2}$ 4   50

6b. $\frac{80.7}{10}$ is closest to

$\frac{1}{4}$ $\frac{1}{2}$ 4   8

7a. $\frac{50}{9}$ is closest to

450   250   10   5

7b. $\frac{50}{9} \times 20$ is closest to

9,000   900   450   100

Mixing It Up

1. Multiply $1\frac{4}{5} \times \frac{1}{2}$. First break down the mixed number.

$$\frac{\boxed{}}{5} + \frac{4}{5} \qquad 1\frac{4}{5} \times \frac{1}{2} = \frac{\boxed{}}{\boxed{}} \times \frac{1}{2} = \frac{\boxed{}}{\boxed{}}$$

Improper

2. Fill in the missing boxes to find $1\frac{4}{5} \times \frac{3}{4}$.

$$1\frac{4}{5} \times \frac{3}{4} = \frac{\boxed{}}{\boxed{}} \times \frac{3}{4} = \frac{\boxed{}}{\boxed{}} = \underline{\hspace{2cm}}$$

Improper   *Mixed Number*

3. Find $1\frac{4}{5} \times 1\frac{3}{4}$.

$$1\frac{4}{5} \times 1\frac{3}{4} = \frac{\boxed{}}{\boxed{}} \times \frac{\boxed{}}{\boxed{}} = \frac{\boxed{}}{\boxed{}} = \underline{\hspace{2cm}}$$

Improper   *Improper*   *Mixed Number*

4. Do the following problems without a calculator. Leave a trail of your work. Simplify your answers. The first one is done for you.

a. $1\frac{2}{3} \times 2\frac{2}{5} =$

$\frac{\cancel{5}}{\cancel{3}} \times \frac{\cancel{12}^{4}}{\cancel{5}} = \frac{4}{1} = 4$

b. $3\frac{2}{3} \times 1\frac{2}{3} =$

c. $\frac{2}{3} \times 3\frac{3}{4} =$

d. $4\frac{1}{5} \times 5\frac{1}{4} =$

e. $100 \times 9\frac{9}{10} =$

f. $3\frac{1}{3} \times 5 =$

g. $2\frac{1}{7} \times 1\frac{3}{5} \times 5\frac{1}{4} =$

h. $4\frac{2}{5} \times 1\frac{1}{5} \times 3\frac{4}{7} =$

Trips on a Number Line

Another way to think of numbers is to arrange them on a **number line**.

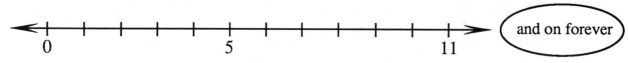

and on forever

1. Put a dot and a label for 8, $8\frac{1}{2}$, $3\frac{1}{2}$, and $10\frac{1}{2}$ on the number line above.

2. The scale or region of the number line will depend upon the numbers you want to work with. The number line below is torn. We can only see 0 to 3 and 19 to 22.

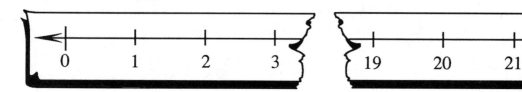

   Put a dot and a label for $2\frac{1}{3}$, $\frac{60}{3}$, and $21\frac{2}{3}$ on the torn number line.

3. The following number line is *calibrated*, or evenly divided, by 200. Calibrate the number line to show 100, 300, 500, and 700.

$655\frac{2}{3}$

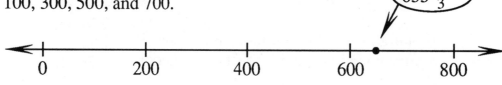

4a. The dot that is labeled $655\frac{2}{3}$ is in an approximate place. Put a dot and label in the approximate places for 51, 290, $179\frac{1}{5}$, $180\frac{3}{5}$, and $773\frac{4}{5}$ on the number line above.

4b. What do you notice about the dots for $179\frac{1}{5}$ and $180\frac{3}{5}$? _____

_____

5. Zoom in and see a small piece of this number line as shown below. The space between 179 and 180 on the number line is called a *unit space*. Each unit space has tick marks dividing it into fifths. Put a dot and label for $179\frac{1}{5}$, $180\frac{3}{5}$, $182\frac{1}{5}$, and $179\frac{5}{5}$ on this number line.

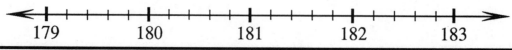

Using a Number Line to Multiply

1. Write the answer to the following problem as a mixed number in lowest terms.

   $6 \times \frac{3}{5} =$ _____

2. Use a number line to do $6 \times \frac{3}{5}$. The following number line is calibrated in fifths. A kangaroo makes 1 jump $\frac{3}{5}$ of a unit long. To do $6 \times \frac{3}{5}$, she needs to make 6 jumps.

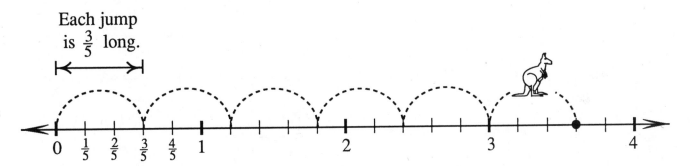

2a. Where did the kangaroo land? _____

2b. Does Problem 2a agree with your answer to Problem 1? _____
   Yes or No

3. Notice that after 5 jumps the kangaroo landed on a whole number. Where did she land? _____

4. If the kangaroo starts at 0 and makes 10 jumps, where would she land?

   Answer _____

5. If the kangaroo starts at 0 and makes 20 jumps, where would she land?

   Answer _____

6. Where does she land after 25 jumps? _____

7. Where does she land after 100 jumps? _____

8. Calibrate the number lines and make jumps to do the following problems. The first two number lines are calibrated for you.

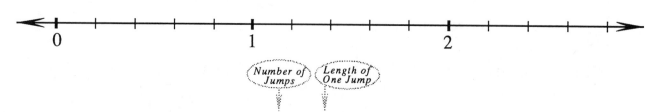

8a. On the number line above, $3 \times \frac{3}{5} =$ _____

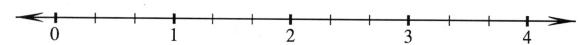

8b. On the number line above, $4 \times \frac{2}{3} =$ _____

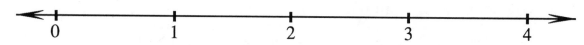

 8c. On the number line above, $5 \times \frac{3}{4} =$ _____

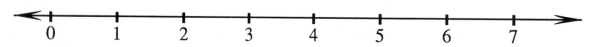

8d. On the number line above, $1\frac{1}{2} \times 5 =$ _____

The following multiplication problem describes the total distance traveled.

Arithmetic with Zero Can Be Tricky

1. How many jumps that are 3 units long does it take to get from 0 to 6? Draw them on the number line.

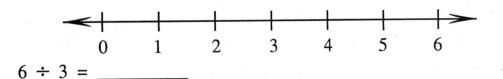

    6 ÷ 3 = _____

2. How many jumps that are 2 units long does it take to get from 0 to 6? Draw them on the number line.

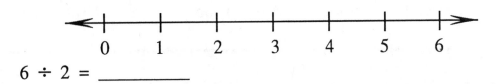

    6 ÷ 2 = _____

3. How many jumps of $\frac{1}{2}$ of a unit length does it take to go from 0 to 6? Draw them on the number line.

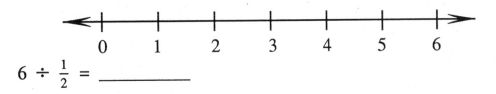

    $6 \div \frac{1}{2}$ = _____

4. How many jumps of $\frac{1}{10}$ of a unit length does it take to go from 0 to 6? Imagine the rest of the jumps.

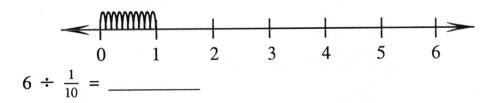

    $6 \div \frac{1}{10}$ = _____

5. How many jumps of $\frac{1}{1,000}$ does it take to get from 0 to 6? You cannot show a jump of $\frac{1}{1,000}$ on the number line above. Imagine it.

    $6 \div \frac{1}{1,000}$ = _____

6. How many jumps of **zero (0)** length does it take to go from 0 to 6?

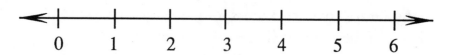

6a. Ten jumps of **zero** end up at **zero**!

1,000 jumps of zero end up at _____.

6b. 100,000,000 jumps of zero end up at _____.

6c. 6 ÷ 0 = _____

The number 6, or any other number, can **never** be reached if the jumps
are zero long. In the problem 6 ÷ 0, the only answer is, "There is no
answer."

---

7. Complete the following problems. Write "NA" if there is "no answer."

a. $0 \times 3\frac{1}{2}$ = _____

b. $15\frac{16}{17} \times 0$ = _____

c. $0 \div 1,623$ = _____

d. $1,623 \div 0$ = _____

e. $0 \times (52 + 8)$ = _____

f. $\frac{0}{1,357}$ = _____

Reciprocals

1. The **reciprocal** of 2 is $\frac{1}{2}$. The **reciprocal** of $\frac{1}{5}$ is 5.

The **reciprocal** of $\frac{2}{3}$ is $\frac{3}{2}$.

1a. What is the reciprocal of 10? _____

1b. What is the reciprocal of $\frac{3}{4}$? _____

1c. What is the reciprocal of $\frac{1}{100}$? _____

1d. What is the reciprocal of 78? _____

1e. What is the reciprocal of $\frac{18}{5}$? _____

2. Notice that the following number line shows 0 to 8.

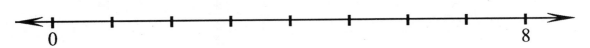

2a. What is the reciprocal of 2? _____

2b. Draw a dot on 2. Then draw a jump from 2 to the reciprocal of 2.

2c. What is the reciprocal of 4? _____

2d. Draw a dot on 4. Then draw a jump from 4 to the reciprocal of 4.

2e. What is the reciprocal of 5? _____

2 f. Draw a dot on 5. Then draw a jump from 5 to the reciprocal of 5.

2g. What is the reciprocal of 8? _____

2h. Draw a jump from 8 to its reciprocal.

2 j. As the whole numbers get bigger, their reciprocals get _____.

2k. What is the reciprocal of 1? _____

2m. Draw and label a dot on the number line to show the reciprocal of 1.

3. On this sheet of paper, it is difficult to have large numbers and still be able to see the space between 0 and 1. Imagine a long ribbon of adding machine tape that goes out to 1,000.

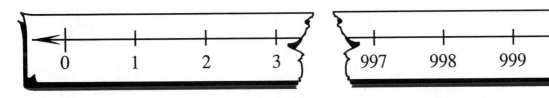

3a. What is the reciprocal of 1,000? _____

3b. Draw and label a dot on the number line to show the reciprocal of 1,000.

3c. Where are all the reciprocals of whole numbers located on a number line?

_____

3d. As the whole numbers get bigger, their reciprocals get closer to _____.

4. Multiply each of the following numbers by its reciprocal.

a. $3 \times \dfrac{\Box}{\Box} = $ _____

b. $\dfrac{1}{3} \times \dfrac{\Box}{\Box} = $ _____

c. $\dfrac{\Box}{\Box} \times \dfrac{1}{7} = $ _____

d. $\dfrac{\Box}{\Box} \times 7 = $ _____

 e. $\dfrac{2}{19} \times \dfrac{\Box}{\Box} = $ _____

f. $4\dfrac{1}{2} \times \dfrac{\Box}{\Box} = $ _____

5. When you multiply a number by its reciprocal, the product is _____.

6a. The reciprocal of 4 is $\dfrac{1}{4}$. Write $\dfrac{1}{4}$ as a decimal. _____

$\boxed{1/x}$ is the reciprocal key, sometimes called the "one over x" key.

 6b. To find the reciprocal of 4, press $\boxed{4}$ $\boxed{1/x}$. _____

Should agree with Problem 6a.

$\boxed{4}$ $\boxed{1/x}$ means $\dfrac{1}{4}$ or $1 \div 4$ which is 0.25.

6c. To find the reciprocal of .25, press $\boxed{.25}$ $\boxed{1/x}$. _____

In decimal form, the reciprocal of 0.25 is 4 and the reciprocal of 4 is 0.25.

 7a. Look at the following keystrokes.

$\boxed{4}$ $\boxed{1/x}$ $\boxed{1/x}$ $\boxed{1/x}$ $\boxed{1/x}$ $\boxed{1/x}$

Is the answer "4" or the "reciprocal of 4?" _____

 7b. Now press the keystrokes. Do you agree with Problem 7a? _____

Yes or No

7c. If you pressed $\boxed{1/x}$ 50 times, would the answer be "4" or the "reciprocal of 4?"

Answer _____

7d. Why? _____

8. Use ⌷1/x⌷ to find the reciprocals in the table.

	Number	Reciprocal *Decimal Form*
a.		
b.	1	
c.	2	
d.	4	
e.	10	
f.	100	
g.	500	
h.	1,000	
j.	2,000	
k.	6,000	

9a. Write in "0" next to "a" in the table. Use the ⌷1/x⌷ key to find the reciprocal of "0". What did the calculator do?

Answer _____

9b. Why doesn't "0" have a reciprocal? _____

Whenever your calculator thinks you have given it an impossible question, it "locks up." Press ⌷AC/ON⌷ to clear your calculator.

10. When you divide 1 by a number, you get its _____.

> To find the reciprocal of 0.8, divide 1 by 0.8.
>
> This can be written as $1 \div 0.8$ or $\frac{1}{0.8}$.

11. Press: ⌷.8⌷ ⌷1/x⌷ _____
    Copy window.

> To find the reciprocal of $\frac{4}{5}$, divide 1 by $\frac{4}{5}$.
>
> This can be written as $1 \div \frac{4}{5}$ or $\frac{1}{\frac{4}{5}}$.

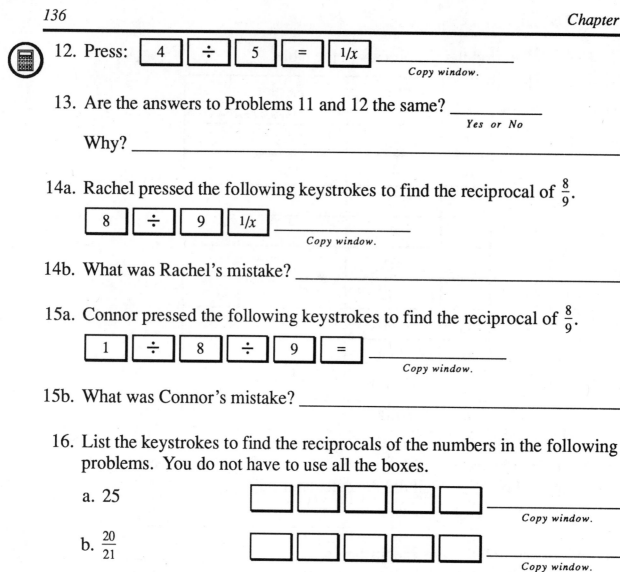

12. Press: | 4 | ÷ | 5 | = | 1/x | _____

                                             Copy window.

13. Are the answers to Problems 11 and 12 the same? _____

                                                       Yes or No

    Why? _____

14a. Rachel pressed the following keystrokes to find the reciprocal of $\frac{8}{9}$.

    | 8 | ÷ | 9 | 1/x | _____

                             Copy window.

14b. What was Rachel's mistake? _____

15a. Connor pressed the following keystrokes to find the reciprocal of $\frac{8}{9}$.

    | 1 | ÷ | 8 | ÷ | 9 | = | _____

                                   Copy window.

15b. What was Connor's mistake? _____

16. List the keystrokes to find the reciprocals of the numbers in the following problems. You do not have to use all the boxes.

    a. 25 | | | | | | _____

                                                   Copy window.

    b. $\frac{20}{21}$ | | | | | | _____

                                                   Copy window.

    c. $3\frac{1}{5}$ _____ | | | | | | _____

         Change to an improper   *Copy window.*

          fraction first.

17a. If you press the keystrokes below, will the answer be more or less than 1?

    | 1 | 1/x | + | 2 | 1/x | + | 4 | 1/x | = |

    Answer _____

                More or Less

17b. Without using a calculator, write the answer in fraction form.

    Answer _____

               Compare with Problem 17a.

17c. Now press the keystrokes to find the answer. _____

                                        Compare with Problem 17b.

Using Number Lines for Division

1. A frog starts at zero and makes jumps $\frac{1}{3}$ of a unit long. Use the following number line to help complete the problems below.

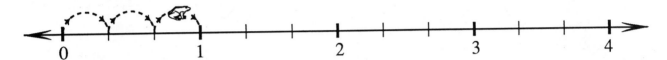

1a. How many jumps will it take to go 2 units? _____ jumps

1b. How many jumps will it take to go 4 units? _____ jumps

1c. How many jumps will it take to go 8 units? _____ jumps

2a. In the problem $2 \div \frac{1}{3}$, think of the following parts. Fill in the number of jumps.

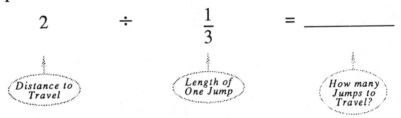

$$2 \quad \div \quad \frac{1}{3} \quad = \quad \text{_____}$$

Distance to Travel   *Length of One Jump*   *How many Jumps to Travel?*

2b. A frog wants to travel 4 units. He makes jumps $\frac{1}{3}$ of a unit long. How many jumps does he travel?

$4 \div \frac{1}{3} =$ _____

2c. A frog wants to travel 8 units. He makes jumps $\frac{1}{3}$ of a unit long. How many jumps does he travel?

$8 \div \frac{1}{3} =$ _____

2d. A frog wants to travel 80 units. He makes jumps $\frac{1}{3}$ of a unit long. How many jumps does he travel?

$80 \div \frac{1}{3} =$ _____

3a. Do $6 \div \frac{1}{2}$ on the following line. Calibrate the line into $\frac{1}{2}$ unit lengths. Find how many $\frac{1}{2}$ unit jumps it takes to get to 6.

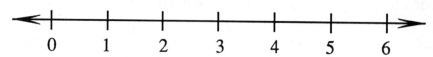

0   1   2   3   4   5   6

3b. $6 \div \frac{1}{2} = $ _____

4. Find $6 \div \frac{1}{10}$ using the following steps.

4a. Each jump is $\frac{1}{10}$ of a unit long. How many jumps does it take to get to 1?

   Answer _____ jumps

4b. How many jumps does it take to get to 6? _____ jumps

4c. $6 \div \frac{1}{10} = $ _____

   You have found the following answers:

   $4 \div \frac{1}{3} = 12$ $6 \div \frac{1}{2} = 12$ $6 \div \frac{1}{10} = 60$

5. Do the following paired problems in your head.

   a. $10 \div \frac{1}{2} = $ _____ $10 \times 2 = $ _____

   b. $7 \div \frac{1}{7} = $ _____ $7 \times 7 = $ _____

   c. $25 \div \frac{1}{4} = $ _____ $25 \times 4 = $ _____

   d. $24 \div 6 = $ _____ $24 \times \frac{1}{6} = $ _____

   e. $100 \div \frac{1}{3} = $ _____ $100 \times 3 = $ _____

6a. What do you notice about the numbers in the paired problems?

   _____

6b. What do you notice about the answers to the paired problems?

   _____

$$100 \div \frac{1}{3} = 100 \times \frac{\boxed{}}{\boxed{}} = \underline{\hspace{3cm}}$$

Should agree with Problem 5e.

Reciprocal

Instead of dividing by a number, you can multiply by its reciprocal.

7. Change $6 \div \frac{2}{3}$ into a multiplication problem. Then solve.

$$6 \div \frac{2}{3} = \underline{\hspace{5cm}} = \underline{\hspace{2cm}}$$

Multiplication Problem

8. Solve the following problems in your head.

   a. $4 \div \frac{1}{5} = $ _____   b. $4 \div \frac{2}{5} = $ _____

   c. $4 \div \frac{4}{5} = $ _____   d. $4 \div \frac{8}{5} = $ _____

9. Use the following steps to find $2\frac{1}{2} \div \frac{3}{10}$. Simplify your answer.

$$2\frac{1}{2} \div \frac{3}{10} = \frac{\boxed{}}{2} \div \frac{3}{10} = \frac{\boxed{}}{2} \times \frac{\boxed{}}{\boxed{}} = \frac{\boxed{}}{\boxed{}} = \underline{\hspace{2cm}}$$

Reciprocal   *Mixed Number*

10. Fill in the missing blanks to solve $2\frac{13}{15} \div 3\frac{3}{4}$.

$$2\frac{13}{15} \div 3\frac{3}{4} = \frac{\boxed{}}{\boxed{}} \div \frac{\boxed{}}{\boxed{}} = \frac{\boxed{}}{\boxed{}} \times \frac{\boxed{}}{\boxed{}} = \underline{\hspace{2cm}}$$

Improper   *Improper*
Fraction   *Fraction*

11. Clarissa says, "Since division by 0 is not possible, you can't do the following problem." Is she right? Why or why not?

$$2\frac{13}{15} \div 3\frac{0}{4} = $$

Explain your reasoning. _____

_____

Homework 9: Traveling Through Time

Stay Alert! "×" and "÷" are mixed up on purpose. Simplify your answers.

1a. $12 \div \frac{1}{2}$ = _____   1b. $12 \times \frac{1}{2}$ = _____

2a. $\frac{1}{2} \div 12$ = _____   2b. $\frac{1}{2} \times 12$ = _____

3a. $10 \times \frac{1}{3}$ = _____   3b. $10 \div \frac{1}{3}$ = _____

4a. $1 \div \frac{1}{18}$ = _____   4b. $1 \times \frac{1}{18}$ = _____

5a. $\frac{1}{2} \div \frac{1}{18}$ = _____   5b. $\frac{1}{2} \times \frac{1}{18}$ = _____

6a. $\frac{6}{7} \times \frac{14}{15}$ = _____   6b. $\frac{6}{7} \div 1\frac{1}{14}$ = _____

7a. $5\frac{1}{2} \div 0$ = _____   7b. $5\frac{1}{2} \times 0$ = _____

8. Complete the following problems.

   a. $\dfrac{\boxed{}}{\boxed{}} \times \dfrac{7}{8} = \dfrac{7}{16}$ b. $\dfrac{2}{3} \times \dfrac{\boxed{}}{\boxed{}} = 1$

   c. $8 \div \dfrac{1}{\boxed{}} = 88$ d. $10 \div \dfrac{\boxed{}}{3} = 15$

9. Complete the following.

   a. $25 \div$ _____ equals 100.

   b. $25 \div$ _____ is greater than 100.

   c. $25 \div$ _____ is less than 100.

10. Without using a calculator, figure out the answers.

   a. | 8 | 1/x | + | 8 | 1/x | + | 8 | 1/x | = | _____

   b. | $\frac{1}{2}$ | 1/x | × | $\frac{1}{2}$ | × | $\frac{1}{2}$ | 1/x | = | _____

   c. | 100 | 1/x | × | 50 | = | _____

Maneuvers with Fractions   © *David A. Page*

10. One Good Operation Deserves Another

Addition, subtraction, multiplication, and division are called *operations*.
These operations take two numbers and give back the answer. For example,
multiplication takes 3 and 7 and gives back 21 as the answer. This is written as
$3 \times 7 = 21$.

Problems that involve more than one type of operation can be complicated.
Which operation do you use first? Mathematicians and engineers have agreed
on an **order of operations**. Multiplication and division "outrank" addition and
subtraction.

When you solve a problem, multiply and divide first; then add and subtract
from left to right.

Here is a sample problem:

$$\frac{1}{2} \times \frac{1}{3} \;+\; 4 \times 5 \;=$$

$$\left(\frac{1}{2} \times \frac{1}{3}\right) + \left(4 \times 5\right) =$$

First look
for × or ÷.
Do them.

Now do the
addition. → $\frac{1}{6} \;+\; 20 \;=\; 20\frac{1}{6}$

The following problem has multiplication and division right next to each other.
Since multiplication and division have the same rank, go from **left to right**.

$$100 - 60 \div 10 \times \frac{1}{2} =$$

$$100 - \left(60 \div 10\right) \times \frac{1}{2} =$$

Look for ÷ or ×.
Do ÷ because it
is on the left.

× outranks −

$$100 - \left(6 \times \frac{1}{2}\right) \quad =$$

$$100 - \quad 3 \quad\quad = 97$$

1. Look at how Dena solved the following problem.

$$7\frac{1}{2} - 3 + \frac{1}{2} = 7\frac{1}{2} - 3\frac{1}{2} = 4$$

1a. Dena's answer is incorrect. What is the correct answer? _____

1b. What did she do wrong? _____

2. Solve the following problems without a calculator. Remember to use order of operations. Put a loop around the operation you must do first. The first one is done for you.

a. $2 + \boxed{(4 \times 10)} = \underline{42}$ b. $25 - 5 + 7 = \underline{}$

c. $12 \div 2 \times 3 = \underline{}$ d. $9 - 6 \div 3 + 1 = \underline{}$

e. $\frac{6}{7} - \frac{2}{7} + \frac{1}{7} = \underline{}$ f. $\frac{4}{5} \times \frac{3}{5} + \frac{2}{5} \times \frac{2}{5} = \underline{}$

g. $\frac{1}{7} + \frac{6}{7} - \frac{2}{7} \times 3 = \underline{}$ h. $36 \div 4 \times \frac{3}{4} = \underline{}$

j. $\frac{6}{7} + \frac{5}{7} \div \frac{1}{7} = \underline{}$ k. $\frac{2}{3} + \frac{1}{2} \times \frac{5}{6} = \underline{}$

m. $1 + 2.416 \div 2.416 = \underline{}$ n. $2,416 - 1 \times 2 = \underline{}$

p. $6 + 1 \div 5 + 4 \div 5 = \underline{}$ q. $139\frac{5}{8} + 4 \div 2 = \underline{}$

r. $11\frac{3}{4} + 1 \times 1\frac{1}{4} = \underline{}$ s. $11\frac{3}{4} + 0 \div 11\frac{3}{4} = \underline{}$

Parentheses

1. Solve the following problem without a calculator using order of operations.

   $1.95 + 1.47 \div 3 = \underline{}$

Sometimes you want to add or subtract before you multiply or divide. For example: Helen, Arlene, and Estelle went to the store to buy school supplies. They bought a package of notebook paper for $1.95 and a box of pencils for $1.47. The total bill was $3.42. They divided the total bill evenly so that each student paid $1.14.

In this problem, add first. .... $(1.95 + 1.47) \div 3 =$

$$3.42 \div 3 = \$1.14$$

Parentheses allow you to change the usual order of operations.

WHOOSH .... 👆
$(1.95 + 1.47) \div 3 =$
WHOOSH .... 👆

$$(1.95 + 1.47) \div 3 =$$

Parentheses mean "do this operation first." When you are inside parentheses, follow the order of operations. If parentheses are inside other parentheses, do the inside parentheses first. For example:

$$(100\tfrac{4}{5} + (\tfrac{4}{5} - \tfrac{3}{5})) \times (2 + \tfrac{2}{5} \times \tfrac{5}{2}) =$$

$$(100\tfrac{4}{5} + (\tfrac{4}{5} - \tfrac{3}{5})) \times (2 + \tfrac{2}{5} \times \tfrac{5}{2}) =$$

$$(100\tfrac{4}{5} + \quad \tfrac{1}{5} \quad) \times (2 + \quad 1 \quad) =$$

$$101 \qquad \times \qquad 3 \qquad = 303$$

2. Do the following problems without a calculator.

   a. $7 \times (9 + 1) =$ _____

   b. $(3 + 3 \times 5) \div 6 =$ _____

   c. $(25 \times (16 \div 4)) + 33 =$ _____

   d. $\tfrac{4}{3} - \left(\tfrac{2}{3} + \tfrac{1}{3}\right) =$ _____

   e. $2 + 6 \div \left(\tfrac{5}{12} - \tfrac{5}{12}\right) =$ _____

   f. $\left(\tfrac{7}{15} + \left(\tfrac{1}{3} - \tfrac{1}{5}\right)\right) \times \tfrac{1}{3} =$ _____

3. A fraction bar tells you to think of the whole numerator in parentheses and the whole denominator in parentheses.

$$\frac{49 + 1}{2 + 8} \text{ means } \frac{(49 + 1)}{(2 + 8)}, \text{ which is } \frac{50}{10} = 5$$

3a. What is the answer to $\frac{(40 + 80)}{(20 + 40)}$? _____

3b. Martha pressed the following keystrokes to do Problem 3a.

What was Martha's answer? _____

3c. Martha's calculator knows order of operations. Circle the keystrokes above that show what operation the calculator did first.

3d. List the keystrokes Martha should have used.

☐ ☐ ☐ ☐ ☐ ☐ ☐ ☐ ☐ ☐ ☐ ☐

3e. Press the keystrokes to see if you agree with Problem 3a.

In the problem $\frac{40 + 80}{20 + 40}$, the fraction bar implies parentheses in the numerator and the denominator. Therefore, parentheses must be entered in the calculator.

4. Do the following problems without a calculator.

a. $\dfrac{4 + 1}{1 - \frac{1}{2}} =$ _____

b. $\dfrac{99\frac{1}{2} + \frac{1}{2}}{20 + 5} =$ _____

c. $\dfrac{4{,}637\frac{1}{2} + \frac{1}{2}}{4{,}638\frac{1}{2} - \frac{1}{2}} =$ _____

d. $\dfrac{21\frac{1}{2} - \frac{1}{2} - 1}{3\frac{1}{2} - 3} =$ _____

5. Do the following problems with your calculator.

a. $\dfrac{87 - 15}{17.5 - 15.5} =$ _____

b. $\dfrac{90 + 2\frac{1}{2}}{7 - 4\frac{1}{2}} =$ _____

c. $\dfrac{90 + 2 \times 1\frac{1}{2}}{35 - 8 \times \frac{1}{2}} =$ _____

d. $9 + \dfrac{9\frac{5}{7} + 2\frac{4}{7} + 8\frac{1}{7}}{3 - 1\frac{3}{7}} =$ _____

11. One in a Million

1a. Estimate how many stars are on this page. _____

1b. Find the number of stars. _____

1c. Find the number of circles. _____

The air around you is made up of about $\frac{3}{4}$ **nitrogen** and about $\frac{1}{4}$ **oxygen**, but there are many other gases in the air. All living things, including you, need oxygen to transform food into energy to move and grow. When you use oxygen, you breathe out **carbon dioxide**. Plants take in carbon dioxide and give off oxygen. This is one of the many cycles in nature.

There is not much carbon dioxide in the air — even though it is very important. Out of 10,000 gas molecules in a clean-air sample, 3 of them are carbon dioxide. You can get an idea of $\frac{3}{10,000}$ from the star and circle page. There are 10,000 shapes (9,997 stars and 3 circles) on the page. So $\frac{3}{10,000}$ are circles.

2a. As a class, make 100 copies of the star and circle sheet and put them on a wall in your classroom. How many **circles** are there on the wall?

Answer _____ circles

2b. How many shapes are there altogether? _____ shapes

$\frac{3}{10,000}$ of one sheet are circles. $\frac{300}{1,000,000}$ of the 100 sheets are circles. These fractions are equal and can be written as the following proportion.

$$\left(\begin{array}{c}1\\ \text{Sheet}\end{array}\right) \cdots\, \frac{3}{10,000} = \frac{300}{1,000,000} \,\cdots \left(\begin{array}{c}100\\ \text{Sheets}\end{array}\right)$$

In scientific work, it is customary to abbreviate $\frac{300}{1,000,000}$ as 300 ppm. This means 300 **parts per million**.

3a. Write $\frac{2}{1,000,000}$ in parts per million (ppm).

$\frac{2}{1,000,000}$ = _____ parts per million (ppm)

3b. Write $\frac{200}{1,000,000}$ in parts per million (ppm).

$\frac{200}{1,000,000}$ = _____ ppm

3c. Which fraction is larger? _____

Use the star and circle sheet (page 145) to answer the following questions.

4. Put a box around five of the stars. What is the fraction of boxed stars?

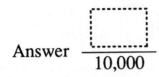

Answer $\dfrac{}{10,000}$

5a. To find the number of boxed stars in parts per million, think of parts per million as a fraction. Then set up a proportion using your answer from Problem 4.

Answer $\dfrac{}{10,000} = \dfrac{}{1,000,000}$

5b. The fraction that shows parts per million in Problem 5a can be abbreviated by writing the numerator followed by ppm.

Answer _____ ppm ⋯⋯(This is not a unit. This is an abbreviation.

6. Look at the stars in the bottom row of the star and circle sheet. Use a proportion to find how many ppm are bottom-row stars.

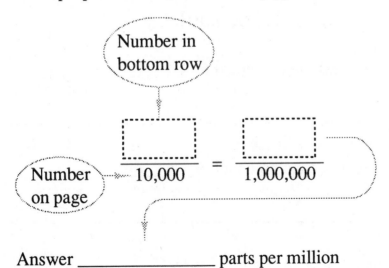

Answer _____ parts per million

7. On the star and circle sheet, suppose triangles (the same size as the stars) were lined up in rows until the white rectangle was filled.

 7a. How many triangles would be on that page?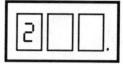

7b. How many total shapes would be on that page?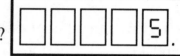

7c. Calculate how many ppm of the page would be triangles using the following proportion.

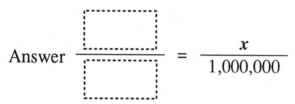

$$\text{Answer} \quad \frac{\boxed{}}{\boxed{}} = \frac{x}{1{,}000{,}000}$$

7d. Write your answer using the ppm abbreviation.

$$x = \boxed{2\ \ 7\ \ \ .}\ \text{ppm}$$

R to the nearest whole number.

Don't Let the Big Numbers Trick You!

 1a. Is $\frac{500{,}000}{1{,}000{,}000}$ greater than, less than, or equal to $\frac{1}{2}$? _____
Greater, Less, or Equal

1b. How did you decide? _____

2a. Is $\frac{499{,}999}{1{,}000{,}000}$ greater than, less than, or equal to $\frac{1}{2}$? _____
Greater, Less, or Equal

2b. How did you decide? _____

3a. Is $\frac{500{,}001}{1{,}000{,}000}$ greater than, less than, or equal to $\frac{1}{2}$? _____
Greater, Less, or Equal

3b. How did you decide? _____

4a. Write $\dfrac{5}{1,000,000}$ using the ppm abbreviation. _____ ppm

4b. Write 500,000 ppm using the fraction notation. $\dfrac{\boxed{}}{\boxed{}}$

4c. Which is larger, $\dfrac{5}{1,000,000}$ or 500,000 ppm? _____

5. Arrange the following eight fractions from largest to smallest. One has been done for you.

$$\dfrac{2}{1,000,000} \qquad \dfrac{1}{2} \qquad 5\ \text{ppm} \qquad \dfrac{71}{100}$$

$$32\ \text{ppm} \qquad \dfrac{2}{10,000} \qquad \dfrac{1}{10} \qquad \dfrac{7}{100}$$

_____   _____   _____   _____
Largest
$\dfrac{2}{10,000}$

_____   _____   _____   _____
                                            Smallest

Don't Confuse Dioxide and Monoxide

1. ***Carbon monoxide*** is a poisonous gas; however, there is **some** carbon monoxide in air. $\dfrac{1}{10,000,000}$ of clean, outdoor air is carbon monoxide. How many ppm is this? Solve for x.

$$\dfrac{1}{10,000,000} = \dfrac{x}{1,000,000}$$

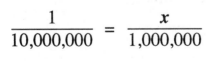

Answer _____ ppm of carbon monoxide

2. In a kitchen with a gas stove, there is often 100 times as much carbon monoxide as there is in clean, outdoor air. How many ppm is this?

Answer _____ ppm of carbon monoxide

3. If a gas stove is poorly adjusted (yellow flame instead of blue), then the concentration of carbon monoxide may get as high as $\frac{1}{30,000}$. Change this to ppm using the following proportion.

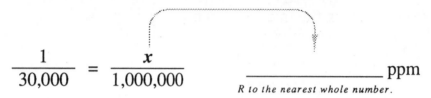

$$\frac{1}{30,000} = \frac{x}{1,000,000}$$ _____ ppm

R to the nearest whole number.

4. Compare the concentrations of carbon monoxide in Problems 1, 2, and 3.

4a. Which concentration is the smallest? _____ ppm

4b. Which concentration is the largest? _____ ppm

5. Inspectors found that $\frac{2}{100,000}$ of the air in Miguel's kitchen was carbon monoxide. What is that in ppm? Finish the proportion and solve for x.

$$\frac{\boxed{}}{\boxed{}} = \frac{x \text{ parts carbon monoxide}}{1,000,000 \text{ parts air}}$$

x = _____ ppm of carbon monoxide

6a. It can be dangerous to breathe too much carbon monoxide. The Environmental Protection Agency (EPA) is concerned when the concentration of carbon monoxide in outdoor air is greater than 35 ppm. One day, the concentration of carbon monoxide in Chicago's outdoor air was $\frac{1,950}{10,000,000}$. What is this in ppm?

Answer _____ ppm of carbon monoxide

6b. Would the EPA be concerned about this level? _____

Yes or No

7. Helium gas keeps dirigibles (blimps) floating in the sky. It also makes toy balloons rise. There is not much helium gas in ordinary air. In one sample of air, $\frac{52}{10,000,000}$ was helium. What is this in ppm? Write and solve a proportion.

_____ Answer _____ ppm of helium

8. Neon is one of the gasses in red "neon light" tubes. There is some neon in ordinary air. The concentration of neon in one air sample was 0.000018. What is this in ppm?

   Answer _____ ppm of neon

9. If you had 1,000,000 parts of air, 18 parts would be pure neon. If you had 7,000,000 parts of air like this, how many parts would be pure neon? Show your work.

   Answer _____ parts of pure neon

Parts Per Billion

The ozone layer prevents the sun's ultraviolet radiation from getting to the surface of the earth. In the air around us, there is 0.02 ppm of ozone. When a concentration gets this small, it is common to switch to **parts per billion, ppb**.

1. Change 0.02 ppm to parts per billion using the following proportion.

$$0.02 \text{ ppm} = \frac{0.02}{1{,}000{,}000} = \frac{\boxed{}}{1{,}000{,}000{,}000} = \underline{\hspace{2cm}} \text{ ppb}$$

2. There is much more carbon **dioxide** in our air than carbon **monoxide**. $\frac{3}{10{,}000}$ of outdoor air is carbon dioxide. Use the following steps to change $\frac{3}{10{,}000}$ to ppm and ppb.

   a. $\frac{3}{10{,}000} = \frac{\boxed{}}{1{,}000{,}000} = \underline{\hspace{2cm}}$ parts per million

   b. $\frac{\boxed{}}{1{,}000{,}000} = \frac{\boxed{}}{1{,}000{,}000{,}000} = \underline{\hspace{2cm}}$ parts per billion

3a. Is 500,000,000 ppb greater than, less than, or equal to $\frac{1}{2}$? _____
                                                                    Greater, Less, or Equal

3b. How did you decide? _____

4a. Is $\frac{500,000}{1,000,000,000}$ greater than, less than, or equal to $\frac{1}{2}$? _____
                                                                    Greater, Less, or Equal

4b. How did you decide? _____

5. Which is larger, $\frac{500,000}{1,000,000,000}$ or 500,000,000 ppb? _____

6. Arrange the following eight fractions from smallest to largest.
   One has been done for you.

   $\frac{2}{1,000}$ 33 ppb $\frac{33}{100}$ $\frac{2}{1,000,000,000}$

   2 ppm $\frac{33}{1,000}$ $\frac{2}{100}$ $\frac{33}{1,000,000}$

                                                                    $\frac{33}{1,000,000}$

   _____   _____   _____
   Smallest

   _____   _____   _____   _____
                                                                    Largest

7a. The smallest amount of "violet" scent that can be detected by a human
    nose is 0.0407 parts per million. Write 0.0407 ppm as a fraction.

    Answer _____

7b. Change your fraction to ppb. Complete the following proportion.

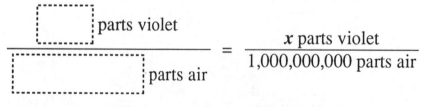

    Answer _____ ppb of violet

8. Nitrogen dioxide gas occurs in **very** small concentrations in ordinary air. Outside, clean air is about 0.000000001 nitrogen dioxide. Change this concentration to parts per billion.

Answer _____ ppb of nitrogen dioxide

9. In a perfume testing lab, two samples of the same perfume are being tested. The concentration of Sample A is 495 ppb, and Sample B is 4 ppm. Which sample has the stronger odor?

Answer _____
Sample A or Sample B

BOY! THAT'S
> COUGH ! <
STRONG STUFF !

10. A common concentration of chlorine in public swimming pools is $\frac{1}{250,000}$. Change this to ppm and ppb.

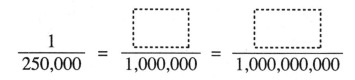

$$\frac{1}{250,000} = \frac{\boxed{}}{1,000,000} = \frac{\boxed{}}{1,000,000,000}$$

_____ ppm of chlorine or _____ ppb of chlorine

 11. If there is 10 times the amount of chlorine in the pool as in Problem 10, what is the concentration in ppm and ppb?

_____ ppm of chlorine or _____ ppb of chlorine

12a. Your answers to Problem 11 are equal. However, only one is used in discussions of chlorine in swimming pools. Which one do you think is used to discuss the concentration of chlorine, ppm or ppb?

Answer _____
ppm or ppb

12b. Why? _____

_____

 13. Circle the smaller concentration. Show your work.

a. There is 150 ppb of a deadly poison.

b. There is 15 ppm of the same poison.

Other Measures by Parts

Parts per million (ppm) and parts per billion (ppb) could go on to parts per trillion, but it is not common to do this. Parts per thousand might be used, but it is also uncommon. **Parts per hundred, pph,** is called percent. *Percent* means "per hundred," and is often written as "%". Cent comes from the Latin word *centum* meaning "hundred." A **cent**ury is a hundred years, a **cent**ipede is supposed to have a hundred legs, and there are one hundred **cent**s in a dollar.

$$100\% \text{ means } \frac{100}{100} = 1 \qquad\qquad 25\% \text{ means } \frac{25}{100} = \frac{1}{4}$$

$$50\% \text{ means } \frac{50}{100} = \frac{1}{2} \qquad\qquad 10\% \text{ means } \frac{10}{100} = \frac{1}{10}$$

When percent is used, it is almost always a **percent of something**.

1. Look at the star and circle sheet (page 145). How many shapes would you circle to show 50% of the shapes?

   Answer _____ shapes

2. How many shapes would you circle to show 25% of the shapes?

   Answer _____ shapes

3a. If you circled 9,997 stars, would the percent be closest to 25%, 50%, 75%, or 100%?

   Answer _____ %

3b. Solve the following proportion to find the percent of stars.

$$\frac{9,997}{10,000} = \frac{x}{100}$$

   Answer _____ %

4a. Noreen said, "There are only 3 circles. That's such a small amount. I think the circles represent about 1% of the shapes." Is Noreen right?

   Answer _____
   Yes or No

4b. If not, how many shapes are 1% of the whole page? _____ shapes

5. Write and solve a proportion to find what percent of the shapes on the page is circles.

   Answer _____%

6a. Cassandra's answer for Problem 5 was 3%. Her percent is the same as what fraction?

   Answer _____

6b. How would you help Cassandra see that she is wrong? _____

   _____

7a. Add your answers from Problems 3b and 5. _____%

7b. What does your answer represent? _____

8. If you put a big loop around 15% of the shapes, how many shapes would that be? Show your work.

   Answer _____ shapes

9. About 780,900 parts per million of air is nitrogen. When numbers get this big, it is common to switch to percent. Use the following proportion to change $\frac{780,900}{1,000,000}$ to percent.

$$\frac{780,900}{1,000,000} = \frac{x}{100}$$

   Answer _____%

   R to the nearest tenth.

10. Fresh air is 209,400 ppm of oxygen. What percent is oxygen? Show your proportion.

   Answer _____%

   R to the nearest tenth.

11. In ordinary air, there is 9,300 ppm of argon. What percent of air is argon? Show your proportion.

   Answer _____%

   R to the nearest tenth.

Homework 11: One in a Million

1. Public swimming pools often have a container of stronger chlorinated water for people to step into before entering the pool. This is to prevent the spread of athlete's foot. One such foot tray has a concentration of $\frac{97}{83,000}$ chlorine. Change this to ppm. Show your work.

   Answer _____ ppm of chlorine
   R to nearest whole number.

2. In most parts of the United States, tap water contains small amounts of fluorine to prevent tooth decay. The recommended concentration is 1 ppm. A concentration of 2 ppm will cause teeth to change color. A concentration of 4 ppm, or higher, is dangerous.

2a. Maneuverville puts 4 parts of fluorine in 5,000,000 parts of water. What is the concentration in parts per million?

   Answer _____ ppm of fluorine

2b. Should Maneuverville put more or less fluorine in their water?

   Answer _____
   More or Less

3a. Fraction City put 1.7 parts of fluorine in 400,000 parts of water. What is the concentration in parts per million?

   Answer _____ ppm of fluorine

3b. Would you recommend that Fraction City change their concentration?

   Answer _____
   Yes or No

4. The land area of Canada is 3,553,000 square miles. It is known that 35% of Canada's land is woodland. How many square miles is that?

   Answer _____ square miles
   R to the nearest thousand.